Contents

Word Analysis

● Read each sentence. The underlined word may be new to you. Use what you know about word parts, syllables, and letter sounds to figure out what the word is. Then write the letter of the meaning on the line before the sentence.

_____ 1. The roads were <u>impassable</u> because of the heavy snow.
    a. wet
    b. impossible to drive on
    c. cleared

_____ 2. The homeless puppy was in <u>pitiable</u> condition.
    a. beautiful
    b. average
    c. causing pity

_____ 3. One <u>misstep</u> by any one of the climbers would endanger the whole group.
    a. jump backward
    b. wrong move
    c. wrong calculation

_____ 4. There seemed to be <u>innumerable</u> ways of doing the project.
    a. very few
    b. too many to count
    c. easy

_____ 5. The weather was <u>unseasonably</u> warm for March.
    a. too damp
    b. not right for the time of year
    c. not comfortable

_____ 6. We spent an exciting, <u>eventful</u> summer at the ranch.
    a. calming
    b. healthful
    c. filled with action

_____ 7. Julie's <u>inconsiderate</u> remark hurt Tommy's feelings.
    a. thoughtful
    b. thoughtless
    c. careful

Name _____ Date _____

Vocabulary

- Read these sentences. Then find the meaning for each underlined word. Mark the space for the answer.

1. Damon is very responsible. You can count on him to do whatever he says he will do.
   ○ charming   ○ musical
   ○ dependable   ○ smart

2. The Aswan High Dam in Egypt was built in 1970. It brought irrigation to desert areas.
   ○ crops   ○ watering
   ○ workers   ○ buildings

3. Barbara had never eaten sushi before. She sampled it and found out that sushi is raw fish.
   ○ finished   ○ cooked
   ○ asked   ○ tried

4. Grandma Moses was a famous painter who did not start painting until she was over seventy. Yet she eventually did 1,600 paintings.
   ○ slowly   ○ luckily
   ○ finally   ○ once

5. Marta doesn't like to go places alone, so she asked her friend to accompany her to the concert.
   ○ walk by   ○ go with
   ○ listen to   ○ pay for

6. If you gaze straight at the sun too long, you can hurt your eyes.
   ○ look   ○ touch lightly
   ○ turn   ○ face

7. It was obvious that something was wrong with the plant. Its stem was drooping, and its leaves were turning quite brown.
   ○ plain   ○ hard to tell
   ○ impossible   ○ annoying

8. One of Thomas Edison's inventions helped save time on Election Day. It was a mechanical vote counter.
   ○ easy   ○ wooden
   ○ working   ○ automatic

9. Marilyn's collie saw a cat and started to chase it. Luckily, Marilyn seized the dog's collar in time to stop him.
   ○ noticed   ○ straightened
   ○ put on   ○ grabbed

10. For most plants, sunlight and water are necessary for growth.
    ○ often   ○ useless
    ○ needed   ○ not enough

11. Rick's mother was a pilot, so he often had an opportunity to ride in a plane.
    ○ wish   ○ need
    ○ chance   ○ job

12. Columbus sought a path from Europe to Asia. Instead of finding it, he landed in America.
    ○ believed in   ○ looked for
    ○ needed   ○ ignored

Name _____   Date _____

Main Idea

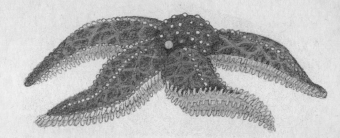

● Read each paragraph. Then write the main idea of the paragraph on the lines below.

1. In pioneer days, no mailcarrier delivered mail right to the door. Instead, young riders and sturdy ponies carried mail by what was aptly named the pony express. A young rider, carrying a mail pouch, would race at top speed from one express station to the next. Here, the exhausted pony would be exchanged for a fresh one. The rider would then race to the next lonely station, usually about fifteen miles away. This system really worked. Only once was the mail lost in all those difficult miles.

_____

_____

_____

2. Have you ever visited a printing plant or seen a printing press? You may think such things have little to do with you — but you would be wrong. Much of the information you need every day comes from printed materials. Think about the books and magazines you read, both in and out of school. Where would you be without signs to help you get around and labels to let you know what things are? Don't forget telephone directories and newspapers.

_____

_____

_____

3. Starfish are sea animals that are found in most oceans of the world, but they are not really fish! Starfish "crawl" through the water on their five "arms." Each of these arms has tube feet, an eyespot, and a suction cup. The starfish's arms grow out from a central disk. Its mouth is located on the underside of this central disk. The starfish can grip a shellfish, such as an oyster, with its suction cups, and pull the shell apart far enough to get the oyster into its mouth.

_____

_____

_____

4. A person who feels strong and lively, looks healthy, and lives a long time is probably one who is active in some kind of physical exercise. Physical activity makes a person's muscles stronger and less prone to sag and strain; it keeps a person's heart and lungs more efficient and less prone to disease. Activity is often important to a person's feeling of well-being and happiness. Physical exercise is more than a few toe touches to keep the waistline trim.

_____

_____

_____

Name _____   Date _____

Predicting Outcomes

● Read each paragraph. Then answer the question below it.

The Lions were leading the Tigers 4 to 1. As the Tigers went to bat for the last time in the game, they had to face Matheson, the Lions' best pitcher. Matheson looked very strong, as he had throughout the game. The Tigers' luck was not changing either; Matheson quickly struck out the first two batters.

1. Which team seems more likely to win? Why? _____

_____

The next batter for the Tigers got a base hit. Then, all of a sudden, Matheson seemed to tire. The next two batters also hit safely, and one run was scored. Matheson walked a batter, and the bases were loaded. The crowd, which had been quiet, began to cheer. Bartell, the Tigers' best hitter, was coming to bat.

2. Which team now seems more likely to win? Why? _____

_____

Bartell was fooled by Matheson's first pitch. She swung wildly and missed. The next pitch was another strike. Bartell hit the third pitch—a long drive to left field, but it was a foul ball. The crowd quieted down again as Matheson looked for the sign from the catcher. Bartell waited, with a determined look on her face. The base runners took their leads. The defense nervously watched, waiting for the pitch.

3. Who do you think will win? Why? _____

_____

_____

Name _____ Date _____

Dictionary

Guided Practice

round | rub

row¹ (rō) *n.*   **1.** A series of persons or things placed next to each other, usually in a straight line.   **2.** A line of seats running across a theater, classroom, etc.

row² (rō) *v.*   **1.** To propel (a boat) with oars.   **2.** To carry in a boat propelled by oars. -*n.*   **1.** A shift at the oars of a rowboat.   **2.** A trip in a rowboat.

row³ (rou) *n.*   **1.** A noisy quarrel or fight.   **2.** A loud noise. -*v.* to quarrel noisily.

1. _____   **2.** _____

_____

3. ____ rough   ____ route   ____ royal   ____ rude

_____

4. The Smith family was looking forward to a **row** on the lake.

_____

5.   slow   now

_____

pre·de·ter·mine (prē′ dĭ tûr′ mĭn)
pre·dic·a·ment (prĭ dĭk′ ə mənt)

6. _____   **8.** _____

7. _____   **9.** _____

ă pat / ā pay / â care / ä father / ĕ pet / ē be / ĭ pit / ī pie / î fierce / ŏ pot / ō go / ô paw, for / oi oil / o͝o book / o͞o boot / ou out / ŭ cut / û fur / *th* the / th thin / hw which / zh vision / ə ago, item, pencil, atom, circus

Name _____   **Date** _____

Dictionary • Word Meanings

● Look at the sample dictionary and pronunciation key. Then choose the best answer to each item. Circle the letter of the answer. For the starred item, mark the space for the answer.

1. Which of these words is the third entry word on the page?
   a. object¹   **b.** object²   **c.** obliterate

2. Which of these words would appear on the part of the dictionary page that you cannot see?
   a. obey   **b.** oboe   **c.** octopus

3. If the word *oblong* were added to the dictionary, which entry word would it follow?
   a. object²   **b.** obliterate   **c.** obscure

4. Which of these entry words may be pronounced two different ways?
   a. object   **b.** obscure   **c.** occupy

5. Which word in the pronunciation key shows how to pronounce the third syllable in the word *occupy*?
   a. pat   **b.** pit   **c.** pie

6. What part of speech is *obscure* in this sentence: "We walked carefully down the obscure staircase"?
   a. noun   **b.** verb   **c.** adjective

7. Which two syllables are stressed in *obliterate*?
   a. first and second
   b. second and third
   c. second and fourth

★ Find the second meaning of the word *occupy*. Which of the following sentences illustrates the meaning?

○ A new family now occupies the house on the corner.
○ The troops took over the city and occupied the palace.
○ Grandfather is retired, but he occupies his time with hobbies.
○ Ms. Berns will soon occupy the office of the president.

object   octagon

ob·ject¹ (ŏb′jĭkt) *n.* **1.** A thing that has shape and can be seen. **2.** A thing being viewed or studied. **3.** A person or thing to which an emotion is directed. **4.** A purpose or goal.
ob·ject² (əb jĕkt′) *v.* **1.** To be opposed. **2.** To say in opposition or protest.
o·blit·er·ate (ə blĭt′ə rāt′) *v.* **1.** To do away with completely. **2.** To cover or hide from view.

ob·scure (əb skyo͝or′) *adj.* **1.** Hard to understand. **2.** Not well known. **3.** Dark or dim. **4.** Indistinct: obscure writing. —*v.* **1.** To hide from view. **2.** To make difficult to understand.
oc·cu·py (ŏk′yə pī′) *v.* **1.** To take possession of and maintain control over by force. **2.** To fill or take up. **3.** To dwell or inhabit. **4.** To hold or control in an office.

ă pat / ā pay / â care / ä father / ĕ pet / ē be / ĭ pit / ī pie / î fierce / ŏ pot / ō go / ô paw, for / oi oil / o͝o book / oo boot / ou out / ŭ cut / û fur / *th* the / th thin / hw which / zh vision / ə ago, item, pencil, atom, circus

Name _____ Date _____

Henry Reed's Engineering Problem

● Complete the story by writing a word from the box on each blank line. The first one has been done for you.

culvert	astute	investigate	detour	batteries
gravel	matters	observation	results	construction

As I looked around the two-square-block ___construction___ site, I knew I was in trouble. How could I find my flashlight in a place like this? Even if I did, the _____ might be dead by now. But it was getting dark, and I really needed it. So I kept on looking.

I walked around _____ signs, crept through a corrugated _____, and climbed over a tall pile of _____. It looked pretty hopeless.

Suddenly, from the other side of a power-shovel, a voice said, "Have you lost something? Perhaps I can help. My powers of _____ are great. I can spot anything within a mile, and I can make _____ deductions about anything I find. Shall I _____?"

As I came around the power-shovel, he was still talking. "Leave _____ to me," he was saying. "I always get _____. I'm a real bloodhound."

I agreed to let him handle the matter, although he looked more like a beagle to me.

Name _____   Date _____

Henry Reed's Engineering Problem

● Think about the story "Henry Reed's Engineering Problem." Decide whether each statement below is true or false, and circle that answer. Then write a reason for your answer. The first one has been done for you.

1. Uncle Al's driveway and lawn were

   often flooded after a rainstorm.

   (True)   False

   The culvert became clogged with leaves and debris, and the water could not run through.

   _____

2. Henry worried when he heard Agony on the other side of
   the road.   True   False

   _____

   _____

3. Agony and the rabbit ran quickly through the culvert.
   True   False

   _____

   _____

4. When he was freed, Agony raced away because he was
   frightened.   True   False

   _____

   _____

5. Uncle Al was impressed by Henry's success in getting a larger
   culvert put in.   True   False

   _____

   _____

Name _____   Date _____

Card Catalog

● Read each question. Decide which type of card you would use to answer the question. In the first column after the question, write the letter **A** if you would look for an *author* card, **T** if you would look for a *title* card, and **S** if you would look for a *subject* card. In the second column, write the letters of the card catalog drawer in which you would find the card. The first one has been done for you.

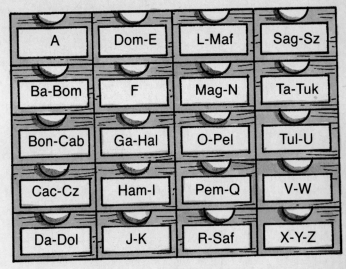

	Type of Card	Card Catalog Drawer
1. What books about Albert Schweitzer does the library have?	S	Sag-Sz
2. Does the library have books about swordfish?	___	___
3. Who wrote *The Ant and the Spider*?	___	___
4. How many books by Gail Moffett does the library have?	___	___
5. Who wrote *The Legend of Sleepy Hollow*?	___	___
6. What books about hurricanes does the library have?	___	___
7. What books about early Olympic competition does the library have?	___	___
8. Which mystery stories by Nan Dow does the library have?	___	___
9. Is *The Bombers* about a basketball or a football star?	___	___
10. Who wrote the *Carpentry How-to Book*?	___	___
11. What kinds of books did Oliver Saint-John write?	___	___
12. How many books about whales does the library have?	___	___
13. What books by Lawrence O'Toole does the library have?	___	___
14. Who wrote *Sunrise Over the Seas*?	___	___
15. What books other than *Journey to the Stars* did Frederick Fast write?	___	___

Name _____ Date _____

Note Taking

Guided Practice

1. Albert Sabin will always be remembered as the person who developed an oral vaccine to protect people against polio.

2. The atmosphere of Mars, unlike that of its neighbor Earth, is thin, cold, and transparent. It contains 95% carbon dioxide.

---

3. **Indiana**
   ☐ leader in farming, especially grain crops and livestock; also industry, such as steel mills and automobiles

   Indiana
   ☐ farming - grain, livestock
   industry - steel mills, automobiles

---

4. **Zebulon Pike**
   ☐ explored Minnesota - 1805
   discovered Pikes Peak — 1806

   1805
   ☐ Zeb. Pike
   Pikes Peak and Minn.
   1806

The earth has three main parts: the core, the mantle, and the crust. The core is the center. It is made up of an inner core, which is solid, and an outer core, which is liquid. Next comes the mantle. It is divided into zones. Volcanic lavas are formed in one of these zones. The crust consists of two layers. The lower layer is made up of thick, basic rocks. The upper layer is the one we know the most about. It makes up the continents.

_____

_____

_____

_____

_____

_____

_____

Name _____ Date _____

Note Taking

● Read the article. Then use information from the article to answer the question on the right.

Father of the Modern Olympics

The Olympic Games are usually linked with Greece. However, a French person is one of the most important people in the history of the Olympics. His name was Baron Pierre de Coubertin. He is known as the "Father of the Modern Olympics."

The Olympics began in ancient Greece in 776 B.C. The games were held every four years for more than 1,000 years. Then, around A.D. 400, the sacred city of Olympia was destroyed by Goths. The Roman emperor, who also ruled Greece, announced the end of the Olympic Games. More than 1,400 years later, archaeologists found the ruins of Olympia. This discovery excited de Coubertin, who was very interested in sports. De Coubertin visited Olympia and decided to re-establish the Olympic Games.

Few people supported de Coubertin's idea. He didn't give up, though. By 1894, he had won over important sports leaders in several different countries. He also convinced a rich Greek merchant to give the money to rebuild the stadium at Olympia. De Coubertin then set up a system for running the games that is still used today. Finally, in 1896, athletes from ten countries gathered in Olympia to compete in the first modern Olympics.

★ If you were taking notes on how the modern Olympics came to be, which of the following would be the best set of notes? Mark the space for the answer.

○ A French person named Baron Pierre de Coubertin is one of the most important people in the history of the Olympics.

○ begin 776 B.C.; every 4 yrs. for 1,000 yrs.; end A.D. 400 — Goths destroy Olympia

○ Old games end A.D. 400; ruins uncovered in late 1800's; de Coubertin wants new games, gets support; 1896, first new games, ten countries; de C's system for running games still used.

○ 1,400 years after Olympia was destroyed, archaeologists uncovered its ruins. This inspired de Coubertin to re-establish the games.

Name _____   Date _____

Maria Tallchief: Dancer with a Dream

- Read each sentence. Find the meaning that fits the underlined word. Write the word next to its meaning. The first one has been done for you.

1. Mrs. Morris entertained us lavishly with a dinner that ended with four desserts.
2. Alan wanted the leading role so badly that he practiced all week before the audition.
3. Ken was upset about making his debut in a very old theater with broken seats.
4. Helen's dancing was so lyrical I could almost hear her singing as she moved across the stage.
5. The vivid colors in the painting seemed to light up the room.
6. Barbara's dynamic personality made everyone agree with her ideas.
7. Matthew choreographed a scene about the Old West for the dance company.
8. Peggy felt the crowd's hostility as she reported that nothing could be done about the old building.

_____ Full of energy; active; forceful.

_____ Hatred; ill will; unfriendliness.

_____ A first public stage appearance.

_____ Composed or arranged the movements of a dance.

_____ An actor's part in a play.

_____ Brilliant, bright color; sharp and distinct.

_____ Songlike.

___lavishly___ Using or giving in great amounts; generously.

- Write a paragraph using three of the underlined words.

_____

_____

_____

_____

_____

Name _____ Date _____

Maria Tallchief: Dancer with a Dream

● Think about the biography of Maria Tallchief. Circle the best answer to each question below. Then write a reason for your choice. The first one has been done for you.

1. How did the *corps* make Maria Tallchief feel at first?

    confident   (unwelcome)   nervous

    The dancers were unfriendly and did not understand Maria's shyness.

2. How did the *corps* feel about Maria during the Canadian tour?

    indifferent   friendly   jealous

    _____

    _____

3. How did Maria feel about Mr. Denham's desire to change her name?

    agreeable   stubborn   pleased

    _____

    _____

4. How did Mrs. Tall Chief feel about her daughter's health?

    worried   unconcerned   satisfied

    _____

    _____

5. How did Maria feel about performing a solo in *Concerto*?

    timid   confident   worried

    _____

    _____

    _____

Name _____   Date _____

Using SQRRR

- On the next page is a social studies article. Follow the directions below as you use the SQRRR method to study the article.

1. Do Step 1. Make a check by each thing you survey.

2. Do Step 2 with the first heading and write your question

   here: _____

3. Do Step 3.

4. Do Step 4, and write the answer you would recite here:

   _____

   _____

5. Follow Steps 2-4 with each of the other headings.

   Second Heading:

   Step 2: _____

   Step 4: _____

   _____

   _____

   Third Heading:

   Step 2: _____

   Step 4: _____

   _____

   Fourth Heading:

   Step 2: _____

   Step 4: _____

   _____

6. What should your last step, Step 5, be? _____

7. Do Step 5.

Name _____ Date _____

Using SQRRR

Cotton

Cotton is a plant with many important uses. Its white fibers are used to make many fabrics and yarns. From its seeds are obtained oils used in hundreds of foods and industrial products.

(1) Where Cotton Is Grown

Cotton is grown in very warm and dry climates all over the world. The leading producers of cotton are the Soviet Union, the United States, China, and India. Cotton is also grown throughout South America and in Africa. In the United States, cotton is grown mostly in the southern states of Alabama, Georgia, North Carolina, South Carolina, Mississippi, Louisiana, and Texas. The average temperature for good cotton-growing areas is above seventy-seven degrees Fahrenheit. Irrigation can supply all the needed water in places with little rainfall.

(2) Different Types of Cotton

There are more than twenty types of cotton plants, but only eight are grown commercially. In the United States, only two kinds are used. One is a type called "American upland." Seven eighths of all the cotton grown in the world is of this type. These plants grow between two to

four feet high and are smooth with a whitish hairlike covering. The other, or lowland variety, can grow as much as five feet tall. The lowland variety has more seeds than the American upland type. It is usually grown for its seeds instead of its fiber.

(3) How Cotton Is Grown

Today, most planting and harvesting of cotton is done mechanically. First, the dried stalks of the previous crop are plowed under to make long ridged rows. Next, a mechanical planter drops in the seeds, packing soil around each one. Then it becomes important to control the spread of grass and weeds that kill the young plants, called seedlings. Today, these weeds are controlled primarily with chemicals and special fertilizers.

A harvester plows under stalks from the previous cotton crop.

(4) Uses for the Cotton Seed

The seeds of the cotton plant are used as much as the white fiber. The oil from the cotton seed is used in making soap, glue, certain kinds of plastics, and special foods for cattle. The fuzz remaining on the seeds, called *listers*, is used for pillow stuffing and for very soft absorbent cotton.

The whitish hairlike covering of a cotton plant is used to make fibers.

Name _____ Date _____

Reference Aids

- Study the list of reference aids below. Read the questions. Choose the reference aid that best answers the question. Write its letter on the line.

  a. Encyclopedia
  b. Almanac
  c. Atlas
  d. Card Catalog/Computer Terminal
  e. Personal Interview

Where would you go to find:

1. how the mayor feels about her job? _____

2. the history of the railroad? _____

3. the call number for *Myth and Mythmaking*? _____

4. a list of the best paying jobs? _____

5. the hazards of being a firefighter? _____

6. the various landforms found in Nevada? _____

7. an account of Lyndon Johnson's term in office? _____

8. a list of all the senators currently in office? _____

9. biographies of famous American explorers? _____

10. the best route from Buffalo to Albany, New York? _____

★ Choose the best answer to each item. Mark the space for the answer.

1. To find the author of *Harriet Tubman,* you would look in the
   ○ encyclopedia. ○ almanac.
   ○ atlas. ○ card catalog/computer terminal.

2. To find out what states border Colorado, you would look in the
   ○ encyclopedia. ○ almanac.
   ○ atlas. ○ card catalog/computer terminal.

Name _____ Date _____

Dictionary • Word Meanings

● Look at the sample dictionary and pronunciation key. Then write the best answer to each question below.

record   **remnant**

rec·ord (rĕk′ərd) *n.* **1.** Information or facts set down in writing. **2.** The known history of something. **3.** A disk played on a phonograph. **re·cord** (rĭ kôrd′) —*v.* **1.** To set down in writing. **2.** To store sound in a permanent way. **reel¹** (rēl) *n.* **1.** A spoollike device that turns to wind a hose, string, or line. **2.** The amount a reel can hold. —*v.* To wind or pull in on a reel. **reel²** (rēl) *v.* **1.** To stagger. **2.** To whirl around. **reel³** (rēl) *n.* A fast, lively folk dance.	**reg·u·late** (reg′ yə lāt′) *v.* **1.** To direct according to a rule. **2.** To adjust something so that it works correctly. **3.** To control the flow of something. **rel·a·tive** (rĕl′ ə tĭv) *n.* **1.** Related or relating. **2.** Considered by comparing to something else. **3.** Depending on something else for meaning. —*n.* A person related by blood or marriage. **rel·ish** (rĕl′ĭsh) *n.* **1.** A liking or appreciation for something. **2.** Great pleasure. **3.** A spicy sauce made with chopped pickles. —*v.* To enjoy.

ă pat / ā pay / â care / ä father / ĕ pet / ē be / ĭ pit / ī pie / î fierce / ŏ pot / ō go / ô paw, for / oi oil / o͞o book / o͞o boot / ou out / ŭ cut / û fur / *th* the / th thin / hw which / zh vision / ə ago, item, pencil, atom, circus

1. Which word is the second entry word on the page? _____

2. Which of these words would appear on the part of the dictionary page that you can't see — *remote, reconsider,* or *relive*? _____

3. If the word *rehearse* were added to the dictionary, which entry word would it follow? _____

4. Which word in the pronunciation key shows how to pronounce the vowel in the third syllable in the word *relative*? _____

5. Which entry word may be pronounced two different ways? _____

6. Which two syllables are stressed in the word *regulate*? _____

7. What part of speech is *relish* in this sentence: "Joel relished the idea of having an evening without homework"?
_____

8. What does the word *reel* mean in this sentence: "When Dana felt a tug on the line, she started to reel in the fish"?
_____

Name _____   Date _____

Graphs

Guided Practice

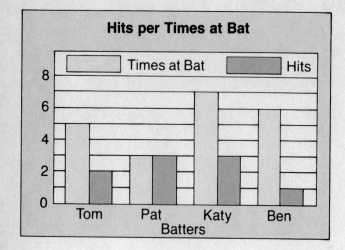

Hits per Times at Bat

1. Who has been at bat the most times?
2. Who has the fewest number of hits?

3. Who got a hit each time at bat?

1. _____ 2. _____

3. _____

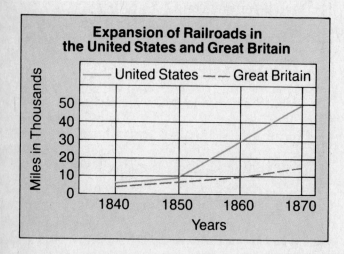

Expansion of Railroads in the United States and Great Britain

1. Which country had more miles of railroad in 1840?

2. In which country did railroads expand more between 1850 and 1860?

3. In what ten-year period was the growth of railroads in the two countries about the same?

1. _____

2. _____

3. _____

Name _____ Date _____

Graphs

● Study the bar graph and the line graph. Use the information
in the graphs to answer the questions. For the starred item,
mark the space for the answer.

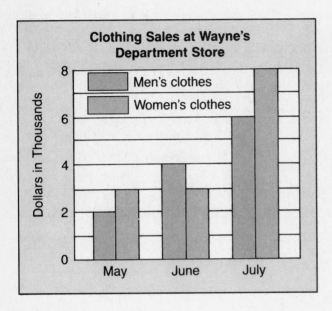

Clothing Sales at Wayne's Department Store

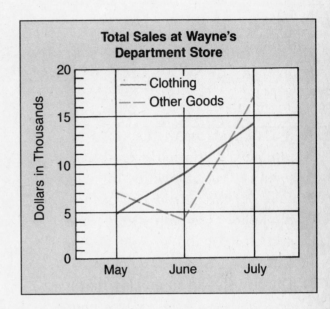

Total Sales at Wayne's Department Store

1. What does the bar graph compare? _____

2. What are the numbers on the left of the bar graph? _____

3. What do the orange bars stand for? _____

4. In which month were men's clothing sales higher than women's? _____

5. During which months did women's sales remain the same? _____

6. What does the line graph compare? _____

7. What does the dotted line stand for? _____

8. In which month were clothing sales higher than those

   of other goods? _____

9. In which month did clothing sales reach $14,000? _____

 What were the total sales of other goods in May?

   ○ $9,000   ○ $7,000   ○ $14,000   ○ $5,000

Name _____   Date _____

Twister!

- Read each sentence. Find the meaning that fits the underlined word. Write the word next to its meaning.

1. <u>Spiraling</u> across the desert, the tumbleweed turned over and over as it was blown by the wind.
2. Jane put the narrow end of the <u>funnel</u> into the empty bottle and poured in the oil without spilling a drop.
3. The fire spread so quickly that it left the entire village <u>devastated</u>.
4. Everyone who saw the <u>menacing</u> shape thought it was a monster.
5. The astronomer's <u>theory</u> that the planet had plant life was proved wrong by the use of the new telescope.
6. If Sam <u>collides</u> with the other skater, both boys will probably fall.

_____ Threatening with harm; endangering.

_____ An idea made up to explain why something happens.

_____ Comes together with a solid impact.

_____ Ruined; laid to waste.

_____ A utensil with a narrow open tube at one end, used in pouring liquids into a container with a small mouth.

_____ Curving in a way that gradually widens.

- Write a paragraph about a tornado, using three of the underlined words.

_____

_____

_____

_____

_____

Name _____ Date _____

Twister!

● Think about the article "Twister!" Below are the names of five things or places in the article. Tell how each was important. The first one has been done for you.

1. Murphysboro, Illinois One of the worst tornadoes in United States history struck the town of Murphysboro. The tornado caused many deaths in Murphysboro and left thousands of people homeless.

2. funnel-shaped cloud

3. Gulf of Mexico

4. National Severe Storms Forecast Center

5. Salina, Kansas

Name _____ Date _____

Noting Important Details

● Read the article, paying attention to the details given about statues. Then follow the directions below the article.

Statues come in all sizes, shapes, and materials. They are one of the oldest forms of art. Scientists have discovered statues in the remains of civilizations that existed more than ten thousand years ago.

In order to last, statues are usually made out of hard materials, such as teakwood, marble, or a mixture of copper and brass called bronze. Statues made from marble or teakwood are carved with sharp chisels. An artist who makes a statue from bronze must pour melted metal into a clay mold so that the metal may harden into the proper shape when it cools.

Statues from ancient civilizations were often small carvings made in jade stone. They were called *figurines* and often represented gods and heroes.

Today, we find much larger statues in a greater variety of materials. Statues are found in parks, in front of museums, and in the lobbies of large buildings. In one way, however, modern statues are like ancient ones: they still commemorate heroes.

There is a famous statue of Benjamin Franklin in Philadelphia, and there is a well-known statue of William Shakespeare in Stratford, England. Yet the most famous statue of all is probably the Statue of Liberty. It is hollow inside. Thin sheets of metal were pounded into shape, then fit over a strong framework. This statue doesn't represent gods or heroes. It represents the idea of freedom.

● Write **Y** before each statement that is correct according to the article. Write **N** before each statement that is wrong. Try not to look back at the article.

_____ 1. One purpose for statues is to commemorate heroes.

_____ 2. There are more than ten thousand types of statues.

_____ 3. On the whole, statues today are used the same way they were used in the earlier centuries.

_____ 4. Statues are a recent invention.

_____ 5. Teakwood is a very hard kind of wood.

_____ 6. One might find a statue in a public park.

_____ 7. Bronze is a mixture of copper and gold.

_____ 8. All statues are carved.

Name _____ Date _____

Note Taking

- Read the article. Then use information from the article to complete the note-taking activities on the right.

Colonial Clothes

Today, most people buy their clothes in stores. In colonial America, however, people made most of their clothes themselves. Making clothes required more than just sewing pieces of material together. The colonists had to begin their clothes-making process at a much earlier stage.

First, the colonists planted flax to use for linen thread. They also raised sheep for wool. Next, they picked the flax and sheared the wool. Then they spun these materials into thread and yarn. They made dyes to color the yarn and then wove it into cloth on looms. Finally, the cloth was sewn into dresses, pants, and shirts.

The whole family worked together to make their clothing. Fathers usually built the looms. Children gathered flowers, berries, and roots to use for dyes and helped to make the dyes. Mothers and daughters spun wool and flax to make yarn and thread. Even very young girls helped. Girls as young as four could knit stockings and hats. Fathers and older children did most of the weaving. Mothers and older children did most of the sewing. Making clothes took lots of team work. Everyone in the family helped!

1. If you were taking notes on how the colonists made their clothes, which of the following items would you include? Underline your answers.

flax and wool spun into thread and yarn
people buy clothes today
flax used for linen
dyes used to color yarn
made dresses, pants, shirts
family worked together
very young girls knitted
yarn woven into cloth on looms
fathers built looms
mothers did most sewing
sheep used for wool

2. Rewrite this sentence into one or two notes: Mothers and daughters spun wool and flax to make yarn and thread.

_____

_____

_____

3. Write four notes of your own about the different steps in clothes making.

_____

_____

_____

_____

Name _____ Date _____

Following Directions
Guided Practice

Write your name in the upper right-hand corner.
Read each sentence. For sentences **1** through **4**, write the
word **True** if the statement is true. Write **False** if it is false.
For questions **5** through **8**, write the word that answers
the question.

John
1. T
2. F
3. F
4. T
5. Florida
6. salt
7. no
8. three

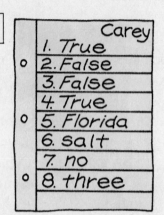

Carey
1. True
2. False
3. False
4. True
5. Florida
6. salt
7. no
8. three

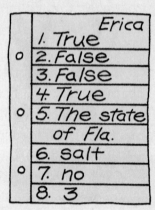

Erica
1. True
2. False
3. False
4. True
5. The state of Fla.
6. salt
7. no
8. 3

Fill a glass with water. Take a length of rubber tubing. Put
one end in the glass and draw some water into it. Now put the
other end of the tube in another glass. The water will flow
through the tube into the second glass. The water will flow through
the tube until the water in both glasses is at the same level.

Materials: _____

Name _____ **Date** _____

Following Directions

● Read the directions for making a stained-glass bird. Underline the answer to each question. For the starred item, mark the space for the answer.

Draw the outline of a bird on a piece of black construction paper. Then, draw several designs inside the bird. Be sure these designs are large enough to be cut out easily. When the drawing is finished, cut out the outlined bird and the designs inside. To cut out each design, first make a small fold in its center. Make a small cut along this fold with your scissors. Then poke one end of the scissors through this cut. To cut out the design, move the paper along the blade of the scissor. Repeat for each design. Then tape or glue pieces of colored cellophane or tissue paper over the cut-out holes on the back of the outline. When the bird is held up to a window or light, the colored cellophane or tissue parts of the bird will appear to light up!

1. When should the bird be cut out?
   a. after the colored pieces have been put in place
   b. after all the drawing is completed
   c. after the designs have been cut out
2. What is the first step in cutting out the inside designs?
   a. A small cut is made in the fold.
   b. The scissors are poked through the design.
   c. The scissors are moved to cut inside the design.
3. What size should the designs be?
   a. as small as possible
   b. whatever size is desired
   c. large enough to be cut out easily

4. What is put over the holes?
   a. black paper   b. nothing
         c. cellophane or tissue paper
5. What is used to keep the colored pieces in place?
   a. tape or glue   b. gum   c. tacks

★ What happens when the bird is held up to the light?
○ The black paper glows.
○ The colored parts appear to light up.
○ The entire bird appears to light up.
○ The bird's wings move.

Name _____   Date _____

Grandpa's Miracle

● Each word in the box is defined in one of the sentences. Choose the word that completes each definition and write it in the sentence. Then write the words in the puzzle. If they are in the right places, by reading down you will find out what Grandpa's miracle was.

cradle	moonstone	insulate
forage	longevity	humidity
	agricultural	

1. A _____ is a pearly mineral used in making jewelry.

2. To hold something very closely is to _____ it.

3. To _____ is to prevent heat from entering or leaving.

4. The word _____ means "long life."

5. To search for food is to _____.

6. An _____ agent is concerned with the care and cultivation of the land.

7. Moisture or dampness in the air is called _____.

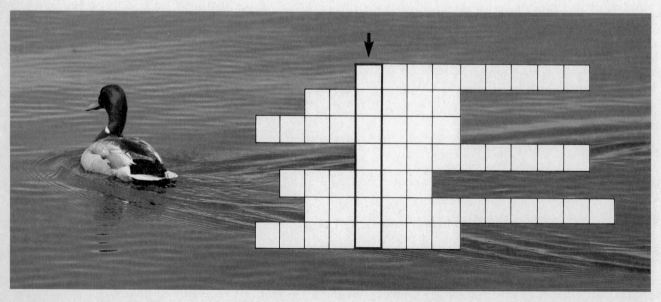

Name _____ Date _____

Grandpa's Miracle

● Think about the story "Grandpa's Miracle." Write two or three sentences that
support each statement below. Use details
and events from the story. The first one has
been done for you.

1. When Grandpa retired, he changed.

Grandpa stopped playing softball with Cathy. He became moody. He no longer helped Cathy's mother in

the kitchen, and he didn't talk to Cathy in the evenings as he used to. He just wanted to be left alone.

_____

_____

2. Grandpa learned a lot about ducks.

_____

_____

_____

_____

3. Grandpa decided the duck was ready to be freed.

_____

_____

_____

_____

4. The duck thought Grandpa was its "daddy."

_____

_____

_____

_____

Name _____ **Date** _____

Reference Aids

● Study the list of reference aids. Decide which one would best help you answer each question below. Write the letter of the reference aid on the line.

a. Encyclopedia   d. Card Catalog/Computer Terminal
b. Almanac   e. Personal Interview
c. Atlas/Globe

Where would you go to find:

1. how it feels to be a school bus driver? ____

2. the author of *Where the Sidewalk Ends*? ____

3. a list of last year's space flights? ____

4. the states surrounding Lake Michigan? ____

5. what books your library has by Scott O'Dell? ____

6. the history of the United States Navy? ____

7. what it is like to do volunteer work at the hospital? ____

8. the location of the countries in Central America? ____

9. **how long a hippopotamus lives?** ____

10. the call number of *Children of the Middle Ages*? ____

11. a list of Super Bowl statistics from 1967 to the present? ____

12. how a hurricane develops? ____

13. the Canadian provinces that border Minnesota? ____

14. what movies from last year made the most money at the box office? ____

Name _____   Date _____

Organizing Information

- Read the article. Then complete the outline using the items listed at the bottom of the page. Remember to capitalize the first word in each main topic or subtopic. Some items have been filled in for you.

Swimming Pools, Old and New

Indoor swimming pools have a long history. In ancient Rome, many wealthy nobles built large pools in the courtyards of their private villas. These pools, called Roman baths, were richly decorated with colorful tiles. They were filled with water from nearby springs.

The first public indoor pools in America were built over one hundred years ago. An enormously large wooden building was constructed right on the shore of the ocean over a beach. It extended out over the water and had a system of long piers for people to walk on and use for diving. At any one time, more than three hundred people could swim in the pool. In the winter, however, the water was far too cold for swimming.

Today's Olympic-sized indoor pools are warmer, safer, and more regular in shape than earlier pools. They are usually rectangular in shape and are fifty meters long. Unlike earlier pools, these are treated with chemicals that kill germs.

Swimming Pools, Old and New

I. _____

  A. Found in private villas

  B. _____

  C. _____

II. First indoor pools

  A. _____

  B. _____

  C. _____

III. _____

  A. Fifty meters long

  B. _____

  C. _____

Roman baths **Temperature controlled** **Filled from nearby springs**
Were built over the ocean **Had long piers** **Decorated with colorful tiles**
Treated with chemicals **Today's Olympic-sized pools** **Were too cold in winter**

Name _____ Date _____

Organizing Information

- Read the article. Then complete the outline using the items listed at the bottom of the page. Some items have been filled in. For the starred item, mark the space for the answer.

Satellites

What Are Satellites?

Satellites have been orbiting the Earth for a long time. Satellites come in all shapes and sizes. They are actually small spaceships without passengers. They are launched into space by rockets. Once in space, they become like artificial moons.

What Do Satellites Do?

Like moons, satellites have their own orbit, or path, that they travel on around the Earth. As satellites orbit the Earth, they receive and send signals from one place on Earth to another.

How Are Satellites Used?

There are many uses for satellites. Communication is one of the most important. There are two kinds of communication satellites. One kind acts like a mirror, bouncing signals from one place to another. Another kind receives signals, makes them stronger, and sends them back down to Earth. Weather satellites take pictures of the Earth's surface. These are used to detect dangerous weather patterns. The satellites also have equipment to measure heat between the Earth and clouds.

Satellites

I. What satellites are

  A. _____

  B. _____

II. _____

  A. _____

  B. Receive and send signals

III. _____

  A. _____

    1. Act like mirrors, bouncing signals

    2. _____

  B. Weather

    1. _____

    2. _____

    3. _____

★ ○ Orbit the Earth
   ○ Measure Heat
   ○ Receive and send signals
   ○ Act like mirrors

Take pictures of Earth's surface	Orbit the Earth	Small spaceships
Receive, strengthen, and send signals	How satellites are used	What satellites do
Detect weather patterns	Communication	Artificial moons

Graphs

- Study the bar graph and the line graph.
Use the information in the graphs to answer
the questions.

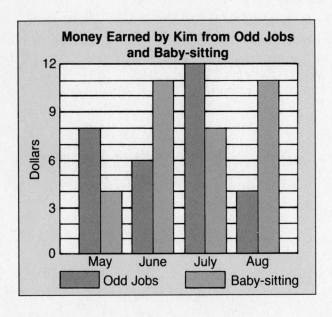

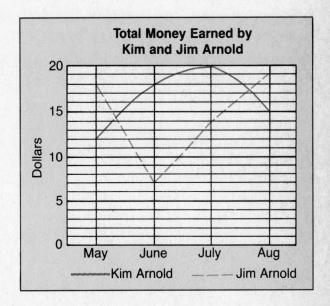

1. What does the bar graph compare? _____

2. What do the pink bars stand for? _____

3. How many months does the bar graph cover? _____

4. What were Kim's earnings from odd jobs in July? _____

5. In which month did Kim earn the least money from baby-sitting? _____

6. What does the line graph compare? _____

7. What does the solid line stand for? _____

8. In which month did Jim earn the least money? _____

9. How much money did Kim earn in August? _____

10. How much money did Jim earn in May? _____

Name _____   Date _____

Taking Notes

Guided Practice

Two Dangerous Reptiles

Some reptiles are small and harmless; others are large and dangerous. Alligators are large, dangerous reptiles. They live in only two places in the world: the United States and China. They grow to be over ten feet long, with large teeth and strong jaws. People often confuse alligators with crocodiles, but alligators have more rounded snouts.

Crocodiles are also dangerous reptiles. The largest of them grows even larger than the largest alligator. Crocodiles live in various tropical areas of the world. They have long, narrow jaws and more pointed snouts than alligators.

Two Dangerous Reptiles

I. _____

   A. _____

   B. _____

   C. _____

   D. _____

   E. _____

II. _____

   A. _____

   B. _____

   C. _____

   D. _____

   E. _____

Name _____ Date _____

Taking Notes

Guided Practice

Machines (Work-Saving Tools)

Machines are tools that help people to do work more easily. One kind of simple machine is the inclined plane, or ramp. With a ramp, a heavy load can be lifted with little effort. The less steep the ramp, the easier it is to lift the load. A lever is another simple machine. This tool has one end longer than the other. Pushing the long end down lets the lever lift a heavy load that is on the short end.

Industrial machines are complex machines that do most of the work in factories. Those used on assembly lines, for example, can help make a product from start to finish. Transportation machines, such as cars, trucks, and trains, are also complex machines. They transport products all over the world.

_____

I. _____

    A. _____

        1. _____

        2. _____

    B. _____

        1. _____

        2. _____

II. _____

    A. _____

        1. _____

        2. _____

    B. _____

        1. _____

        2. _____

Name _____ Date _____

Taking Notes

● Read the article. Then complete the outline, using the items listed at the bottom of the page. Remember to capitalize the first word in each main idea and subtopic. For the starred item, mark the space for the answer.

Wind Instruments

Clarinets and tubas are both wind instruments, but they are very different. The tuba is a long, coiled-up tube. It has a cupped mouthpiece at one end, where the air goes in, and a wide bell at the other end, where the sound comes out. Different notes can be made by pressing the valves on the body of the tuba. Tuba players can also make different notes by changing the tightness of their lips.

The clarinet is a long, straight, wooden tube. Air is blown into a mouthpiece that has a reed clamped to it. The vibrations of the reed cause the air to pass through the body of the clarinet and come out the bell, at the other end. Notes are changed by covering holes in the clarinet. Metal keys over several holes can be pressed to open more holes. This gives the clarinet a wider range of notes.

Wind Instruments

I. Tuba _____

   A. _____

   B. _____

   C. Sound out of wide bell _____

   D. _____

   E. _____

II. _____

   A. _____

   B. Air into mouthpiece with reed _____

   C. Reed vibrations push air _____

   D. _____

★ E. _____

   ○ Notes changed by pressing valves

   ○ Notes changed by lip tightness

   ○ Metal keys for more range

   ○ Long coiled-up tube

Straight wooden tube	**Change notes by pressing valves**
Metal keys for more range	**Long coiled-up tube**
Change notes by lip tightness	**Clarinet**
Air into cupped mouthpiece	**Change notes by covering holes**

Name _____ Date _____

Taking Notes

● Read the following article. Then complete the outline by using the main topics, subtopics, and details listed at the bottom of the page. For the starred item, mark the space for the answer.

Diamonds

Diamonds are valued both for their beauty and for their hardness. Large, clear diamonds are called gem-quality diamonds. They are cut, polished, and used in jewelry. Such diamonds reflect light and break it into all the colors of the rainbow. Small or flawed diamonds are known as industrial-quality diamonds. Their hardness makes them valuable in making tools. Whole diamonds are used for cutting and grinding hard metals. Crushed diamonds are baked onto tools for filing and sawing.

Diamonds can be formed in nature or made in factories. Natural diamonds are formed deep in the lava of extinct volcanoes. Many tons of this lava must be dug up, crushed, and sifted through to find a single diamond. Because diamonds are so rare, people have found ways to make them in factories. The first factory-made diamonds were formed in 1955 by compressing carbon under extreme heat. This method is best for producing small, industrial diamonds.

Diamonds

I. The value of diamonds _____

  A. _____

    1. _____

    2. Reflect and break up light _____

  B. _____

    1. _____

    2. _____

II. _____

  A. _____

    1. Formed in lava _____

    2. _____

  B. _____

    1. Carbon compressed, heated _____

★   2. _____

    ○ Cut and polished for jewelry
    ○ Small, industrial diamonds
    ○ Rock crushed and sifted
    ○ Crushed — saws and files

Natural	**How diamonds are formed**	**Crushed — saws and files**
Gem-quality diamonds	**Industrial-quality diamonds**	**Cut and polished for jewelry**
Factory-made	**Rock crushed and sifted**	**Whole — cut and grind**

Name _____ Date _____

The Boy Who Shaped Stone

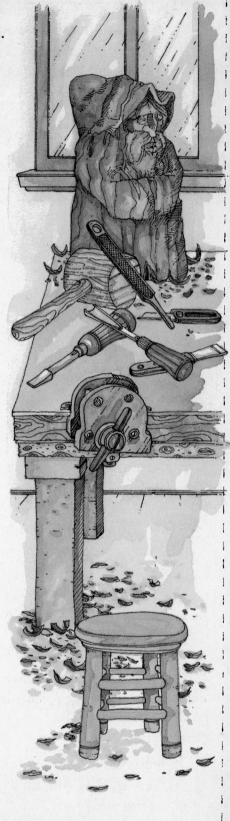

● Each word in the box is defined in one of the sentences. Choose the word that completes each definition and write it in the sentence.

chisel	anvil	deft
flint	axe	apprehensive

1. A person who feels _____ is afraid of something that might happen in the future.

2. _____ is a very hard stone that makes a spark when it is struck against steel.

3. A sharp-edged metal tool used with a hammer to shape wood, stone, or metal is called a _____.

4. A tool with a wooden handle and a sharp metal blade that is used to chop wood is called an _____.

5. People who are _____ are quick and skillful with their fingers.

6. A heavy iron block on which heated metals are hammered into shapes is called an _____.

● Use words from the box to complete the sentences.

1. Tools made from iron are harder and more useful than those made from stone. An _____ with an iron blade can bring down a tree faster than one with a blade made from _____.

2. A _____ made from iron won't chip or flake when hit by a hammer.

3. To shape a pot or a shoe for a horse, a blacksmith may hammer softened iron on the _____.

Name _____ Date _____

The Boy Who Shaped Stone

● Think about the story "The Boy Who Shaped Stone." Complete the sentences below. The first one has been done for you.

1. Great-grandmother's hut was finished first because __all the people in the tribe__ __helped to build her hut before starting work on__ __their own.__ _____

2. Ra had to live in a hut by himself because _____
   _____
   _____

3. Ra had nothing to eat when he went to sleep in his unfinished house because _____
   _____
   _____

4. Ra did not sleep well in his unfurnished hut because _____
   _____

5. Yul wanted Ra to make a new spearhead for him because _____
   _____

6. Ra hesitated to do what Yul asked because _____
   _____
   _____

7. A new "way" was established in Ra's tribe because _____
   _____
   _____

Name _____   Date _____

Following Directions

- Read the directions for cleaning an aquarium. Underline the answer to each question.

Cleaning an aquarium is a job that should be done over two days. First, fill a large glass bowl with tepid water. The water should stand for twenty-four hours in order to reach room temperature. Then gently transfer the fish from the tank to the bowl. Clean the tank with a mild detergent and rinse thoroughly to remove all soap from the gravel and the tank. Before adding clean water, place a piece of paper over the sand or gravel. This will prevent the water from stirring up the material in the bottom of the tank. Fill the tank three quarters full of water, remove the paper, and let the water stand for twenty-four hours. Place the bowl with the fish into the tank. Allow the fish to swim back into the water in the tank. Then remove the bowl.

1. What is the first step in cleaning an aquarium?
   a. move the fish to another tank
   b. fill the tank with tepid water
   c. fill a glass bowl with tepid water

2. What should be done before adding water to the tank?
   a. remove the piece of paper from the gravel
   b. place a piece of paper over the gravel
   c. feed the fish in their temporary home

3. How long should the water stand before adding the fish?
   a. twenty-four hours
   b. several days
   c. twenty-four minutes

4. How should the fish be transferred back to the tank?
   a. by dumping the fish from the bowl
   b. by using a small fish net
   c. by allowing the fish to swim out of the bowl

5. What should be used to clean the tank?
   a. a garden hose
   b. a mild detergent
   c. a scouring pad

Name _____ Date _____

Topic and Main Idea

Guided Practice

A. Many people enjoy roller-skating. It is a sport that requires good balance and quick reflexes. Because this activity can be dangerous, skaters should follow certain rules.

If you roller-skate, be sure to wear pads to protect your elbows and knees. Check your roller skates to make sure that the wheels are well oiled and not loose. Skate only in places set aside for roller-skating. This will help you to avoid people, cars, holes, and small objects found on streets or sidewalks.

_____ 1. **a.** Roller-skating rules
      b. Protective roller-skating equipment
      c. Why roller-skating is dangerous

_____ 2. **a.** Roller-skating is enjoyable but dangerous.
      b. People who roller-skate should follow specific rules.
      c. These rules include staying off streets and sidewalks.

B. Have you ever wondered how plants are able to grow in a hot, dry desert? Some desert trees, such as the acacia, have roots that grow deep enough to reach underground water. Some plants store water in their leaves, roots, or stems. Others shed their leaves to cut down water loss.

Some animals are also adapted to the desert. Insects and spiders have thick body coverings that keep them from drying out. Reptiles have scaled skin that stays moist.

Certain reptiles, such as the tortoise, can change some of their food to water. Many desert animals also stay in the shade or go underground during the hottest parts of the day.

People who live in desert areas have also had to adapt to the heat there. Some desert peoples wear loose clothing that covers them from head to foot. This kind of clothing protects them from the hot sun and from blowing sand.

3. _____

4. _____

_____

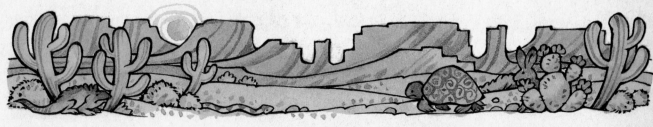

Name _____ **Date** _____

Comprehension: Identifying Topic / Main Idea

Topic and Main Idea

● Read the article. Then follow the directions below.

(1) Spiders use many different methods to help them trap their next meal. Some spiders spin webs. The orange garden spider, for example, weaves an orb web. It has sticky silk that traps approaching insects. This spider spins a new web each day because fresh silk is stickier. Another kind of spider makes a web with silk that is woolly instead of sticky. Thousands of hairs on the web work to trap insects. Still another spider lives in a tent-like web. Hanging from the "tent door" are alarm threads that signal the spider when an insect is near.

(2) Poisoning is another way that spiders get their prey. There are twenty-five thousand known species of spiders. Only thirty are poisonous to humans. However, the bite of spiders is deadly to most insects. Spiders have different kinds of venom, depending upon their prey. Their poison fangs are found at the top of tiny jaws that hang in front of their mouths.

(3) Besides webs and poisons, spiders use other methods to help them obtain food. One spider is a thief. It steals insects that other spiders have carefully wrapped in silk and stored for another day. Another spider "spits" a sticky substance at its victim, thus gluing it to the ground. Jumping spiders leap at their prey, overpowering them in a surprise attack.

1. Write the topic of each paragraph on the numbered lines below.

   (1) _____ (2) _____ (3) _____

2. Write the main idea of each paragraph above.

   (1) _____

   (2) _____

   (3) _____

★ What is the main idea of the entire article? Mark the space for the answer.
○ Spiders use poison to help them obtain prey.
○ The webs that spiders build help trap victims.
○ Spiders are equipped with different means of obtaining prey.
○ There are twenty-five thousand known species of spiders.

Name _____ Date _____

Digging for Clues to the Past / A Small Link with the Past

● Read the clues. Then complete the puzzle using words from the box.

bronze	turf	reconstruct	pottery
copper	cope	salvaging	critical
metals	site	cataloguing	rubble
forces	link	antiquity	pendant

ACROSS

2. Crumbled stone or brick.
5. A reddish-brown metal, easy to work with.
6. Listing in order, with short descriptions.
8. Saving from being discarded or damaged.
9. The location of something.
12. Pots, dishes, and other objects shaped from clay and hardened by baking.
13. Moves or pushes by pressure.
14. Ancient times.

DOWN

1. A yellowish-brown metal made of copper and tin.
2. To build again.
3. A thing that joins or connects.
4. Shiny substances that conduct heat and electricity; most can be melted and hammered into shapes.
6. Using careful judgment.
7. Piece of jewelry attached to a necklace or bracelet.
10. Upper layer of earth containing grass or roots.
11. To deal with difficulties.

Name _____ Date _____

Digging for Clues to the Past/A Small Link with the Past

● Think about the article "Digging for Clues to the Past." Write an answer for each question below.

1. Why are some artifacts destroyed more easily than others?

_____

_____

_____

2. Why is a source of water a promising place to dig?

_____

_____

3. Why must archaeologists dig slowly and carefully?

_____

_____

● Now think about the article "A Small Link with the Past." Write an answer to each of these questions.

1. What was Mary Chubb's responsibility with regard to the necklace?

_____

_____

_____

2. How did the necklace remind Mary of her own past?

_____

_____

_____

_____

Name _____ Date _____

Outlining

● Read the following article. Then complete the outline at the right by using the topics, subtopics, and details listed at the bottom of the page.

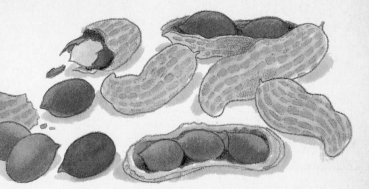

Some Uses of Peanuts

Peanuts have many uses. They are most often used as food. Usually peanuts are roasted whole. They may then be shelled and eaten or used as a flavoring in baked goods. Peanuts are also ground into a pasty spread called peanut butter. In addition, peanut oil that is taken from the peanut has many uses. It may be used for frying and is also used in making vegetable shortenings, such as margarine and salad oil.

In industry, a low-grade peanut oil is used to oil machinery. It is also used in making many personal products, such as soap, face powder, and shaving cream. Peanut shells may be ground into powder. This powder is used to make plastics and wallboard.

On farms, peanut shells are used in fertilizers. The leftover parts of the peanut plant after the peanuts are harvested are sometimes used as hay.

In industry   **Shelled and eaten**   **Shells used in fertilizers**
Roasted whole   **Low-grade peanut oil**   **Used in shortenings**
On farms   **Used to make plastics**   **Used in personal products**
Peanut oil

Some Uses of Peanuts

I. As food _____

    A. _____

        1. _____

        2. Shelled and used as flavoring

    B. Ground into peanut butter

    C. _____

        1. Used for frying

        2. _____

II. _____

    A. _____

        1. Used to oil machinery

        2. _____

    B. Powder from ground shells

        1. _____

        2. Used to make wallboard

III. _____

    A. _____

    B. Leftover parts used as hay

Name _____   Date _____

Locating Information Quickly

Guided Practice

Horses

(1) Types of Horses

Horses are divided into three major categories by size. Heavy horses weigh over 2,000 pounds. They have heavy bones and strong legs. Light horses weigh less than 1,300 pounds. They have small bones and thin legs. Ponies usually weigh less than 800 pounds.

(2) Saddle Horses

The most popular type of horse is the saddle horse. Saddle horses are ridden for pleasure, for work, or for sport.

(3) Famous Horses

Alexander the Great rode his famous horse Bucephalus in many battles as he conquered most of the known world around 330 B.C. More recently, a horse named Clever Hans was taught to respond to signals, which made it seem as though he could solve arithmetic problems.

(4) Feeding Horses

Horses need to be fed three times a day. Horses that are kept inside should be fed hay, grain, and salt. Horses that are kept outside where there is plenty of grass need only grain and salt. Oats are a favorite grain of horses.

(5) Grooming Horses

Horses need to be brushed and combed frequently to keep them healthy and looking good. Their feet require special care. Loose dirt and small pebbles should be removed with a hoof pick.

(6) Riding Horses

A rider should mount a horse from the left side and sit in the middle of the saddle with a straight, but not stiff, back. He or she controls the horse with leg signals and movements of the reins.

1. _____

_____

2. _____

3. _____

4. _____

_____

Name _____ Date _____

Locating Information Quickly

● Skim the title, subtitles, and the first and last few sentences of the article below. Then read each question. Scan the article to answer the question. Write the letter of the paragraph in which the answer is found. For the starred item, mark the space for the answer.

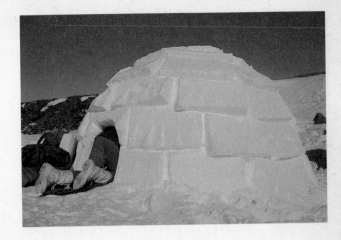

_____ 1. How are igloos lighted?

_____ 2. What does the word *igloo* mean?

_____ 3. How thick are the walls of an igloo?

_____ 4. How does one enter an igloo?

_____ 5. What is the temperature inside an igloo?

★ Suppose you want to scan the article to find out where one sleeps in an igloo? Which paragraph should you read?
○1   ○2   ○3   ○4

Igloos

1. What Igloos Are

Igloo is an Inuit word for "shelter." It refers to tents and sod houses, as well as to the snowhouses that most people think of when they hear the word *igloo*.

2. How Snowhouses Are Made

Snowhouses are made from packed snow, not ice. The snow is cut into blocks that are about three feet long, two feet wide, and one foot thick. The blocks are fitted together in a spiral that gets smaller near the top.

3. The Parts of a Snowhouse

Snowhouses that are used as permanent shelters by the Inuits of central Canada are much more elaborate than the ones that are used as temporary shelters. They have a long passageway that leads to a storage area. The floor of the passageway and storage area is lower than the floor of the main living area. This helps keep the cold winds out.

4. The Inside of a Snowhouse

Small snow platforms are built inside a snowhouse to hold belongings. A large snow platform along the back serves as a sleeping area when covered with furs. Lamps provide light and heat for cooking. A small hole in the top of the dome allows smoke and stale air to escape. The temperature inside a snowhouse rarely gets above 44 degrees Fahrenheit—about the temperature of a refrigerator. The snowhouse, however, is an engineering marvel in its simple design and functional purpose.

Name _____   Date _____

Journey's End

- Complete the story by writing a word from the box on each blank line.

shelving	plunged	glazed	rendezvous	exasperated
eddy	lowing	regarded	footsteps	emaciated

Paul looked worn and _____ from days of drift-ing at sea without food. His eyes were _____ and he could hardly see. Would his cousin wait for him on the small island off the coast? How long had he been drifting? Paul just couldn't remember, and this left him angry and

_____. He _____ his position as hope-less. Like his boat nose-diving into the turbulent water when the _____ caught it, Paul was _____ in gloom.

Suddenly, Paul felt his boat hit the sloped

_____. From a kneeling position, he stared at the shore before him. He couldn't believe he had come to the end of his terrible voyage. He heard the _____ of cows and the sound of human _____. "Well, cousin," he heard a voice say, "what took you so long?"

Name _____ Date _____

Journey's End

● Think about the story "Journey's End." Write two or three sentences that support each statement below. Use details and events from the story.

1. It was only four hundred miles from Joe's house to the Duke's house in Scotland, but Lassie traveled one thousand miles to get back.

_____

_____

_____

_____

2. Joe's mother refused to give up.

_____

_____

_____

_____

3. Joe knew that his parents cared for Lassie as much as he did.

_____

_____

_____

_____

4. The shopkeepers said, "You can set your clocks by her."

_____

_____

_____

_____

Name _____ Date _____

Vocabulary

- Read each sentence. Then find the meaning for the underlined word. Mark the space for the answer.

1. It took four hundred thousand workers and twenty years to complete the <u>construction</u> of the Great Pyramid in Egypt.
   ○ building   ○ taking apart   ○ cleaning   ○ planning

2. Kathy tasted the baked apple, and she thought it had a <u>slight</u> flavor of cinnamon.
   ○ little   ○ strong   ○ unpleasant   ○ sweet

3. Thomas Edison played a <u>significant</u> part in the beginning of motion pictures. One of the first movies was made in his lab.
   ○ starring   ○ careless   ○ important   ○ unimportant

4. Before buying a home computer, Frank's parents examined several kinds in order to make the right <u>selection</u>.
   ○ program   ○ price   ○ use   ○ choice

5. Washington, D.C., became the <u>site</u> of the federal government in 1790.
   ○ view   ○ location   ○ head   ○ building

6. The weather was perfect for a picnic. The sun was warm, and the breeze blew <u>mildly</u>.
   ○ gently   ○ every which way   ○ strongly   ○ loudly

7. It would take about two years for a spaceship to make the long <u>journey</u> to the planet Jupiter.
   ○ study   ○ trip   ○ experiment   ○ landing

8. The <u>intensity</u> of the sun's rays gave Carol a bad sunburn.
   ○ warmth   ○ weakness   ○ strength   ○ spottiness

9. In mathematics today, there are many <u>theories</u>. One says that if a person could travel faster than the speed of light, he or she would go backward in time.
   ○ facts   ○ laws   ○ problems   ○ ideas

10. With the Blue Jays behind in the last inning, Tracy hit a home run. The <u>result</u> was that her team won, 7-5.
    ○ win   ○ surprise   ○ outcome   ○ good luck

Name _____   Date _____

Taking Notes

● Read the article. Then complete the outline, using the items listed at the bottom of the page. Remember to capitalize the first word in each main topic or subtopic. Some items have been filled in for you.

Television People

It takes many people to put on a television program. Some of these people are directly involved in creating the show. The producer is in charge of the whole program. The producer hires staff members and coordinates all the different aspects of the broadcast. The director decides how the actors should move or talk and what the cameras will show to viewers. Script writers create the dialogue, or what the actors say. They also write directions for how to say things and what to do. A musical director chooses music for the program.

Other staff members are responsible for the way the actors and settings look. These artisans include make-up artists, costume designers, and set designers. Hairstyles, clothing, and even furniture are carefully chosen.

Technical details—sound, lighting, and color—are handled by engineers. Camera operators are also part of the technical crew.

Television People

I. Creators

   A. _____

      1. _____

      2. Coordinates everything

   B. _____

      1. Decides what actors do

      2. _____

   C. Script writers

      1. Write dialogue for actors

      2. _____

   D. _____

II. _____

   A. Make-up artists

   B. _____

   C. _____

III. _____

   A. _____

   B. Camera operators

Hires staff	**Producer**	**Artisans**
Write directions for action	**Set designers**	**Know what shots to take**
Costume designers	**Decides camera shots**	**Director**
Engineers	**Composer**	**Technicians**

Name _____ Date _____

Using Context

Guided Practice

_____ 1. The Romans built huge **aqueducts,** structures that carry water long distances, that we still marvel at today.

_____ 2. One lane of the highway was closed, so the flow of traffic was **impeded.**

_____ 3. The mother cat **hovered** around her kittens in the same way that the mother duck stayed close by her ducklings.

---

4. Andy raised his question first. Then it was Marla's turn to **pose** hers.

   a. to present   **b.** position   **c.** to pretend

5. The play was so **melodramatic,** so filled with artificial emotion, that we did not enjoy it.

   a. full of false feeling   **b.** dull   **c.** having too much music

6. The dog scratched and scratched until its skin was **raw.**

   a. not cooked   **b.** damp and chilly   **c.** sore

---

7. The discovery of the ancient city created a lot of **agitation.** It was reported that everything was falling to pieces. Even the statues were beginning to **molder.** Still, they were said to be **exquisite,** absolutely lovely, and photographs of them were in all the newspapers.

| ancient | beautiful | crumble |
| excitement | mixture | turn green |

agitation _____   molder _____   exquisite _____

Name _____   Date _____

Using Context

- Read each sentence. Then choose the best meaning for the underlined word from the definitions in the box. Write the letter of the meaning on the line. For the starred item, mark the space for the answer.

____ 1. The picnic plans were foiled because no one had obtained a cook-out permit from the park.

____ 2. Terry was asked to evaluate the essays, and he judged each one as fairly as possible.

____ 3. The baby was so drowsy that she almost fell asleep in her highchair.

____ 4. Carl looked very solemn when he came out of the principal's office. I had never seen him look so serious.

____ 5. Mother admonished me to clean up my room, so I obeyed her warning.

____ 6. After the hurricane, the area was so devastated that the National Guard was called in to help.

____ 7. Lucy is too shy to initiate, or start, a conversation.

____ 8. The room was so stuffy that Brad thought he would smother if he didn't get some fresh air.

____ 9. When all the pertinent information was in, the detective was able to solve the case.

____ 10. Freda is a very good swimmer, but she feels inadequate when it comes to diving.

____ 11. The President is expected to ratify, or approve, the bill.

____ 12. The crowd was quiet during most of the speech, but when the candidate mentioned raising taxes, people railed against her.

★ When the dam broke, the water deluged the land for miles around.
○ sprinkled   ○ froze   ○ exploded   ○ flooded

a. warned	**e.** not equal to a task	**i.** wrecked, ruined
b. to approve formally	**f.** ruined, frustrated	**j.** objected loudly
c. to begin	**g.** to decide the worth of	**k.** ready to fall asleep
d. to the point	**h.** to suffer from lack of air	**l.** grave, serious

Name _____   Date _____

Thank You, Jackie Robinson

● Use the words in the box to complete the sentences. Then write the words in the puzzle. If the words are in the right places, by reading down you should find something that Jackie Robinson had many of.

remote	vindictive	smugly	deigned
hesitated	consecutive	loaf	literally

1. Liz never _____; she dove right in.

2. On hot days, Andy likes to _____ around the pool.

3. Beth lived on a mountain ranch, _____ from any city.

4. I was surprised that the queen _____ to speak to me.

5. Martha was joking, but Steve took her words _____.

6. Mark scored three _____ goals during the hockey game.

7. The team felt _____ and promised revenge.

8. Pleased with winning the contest, Josh smiled _____.

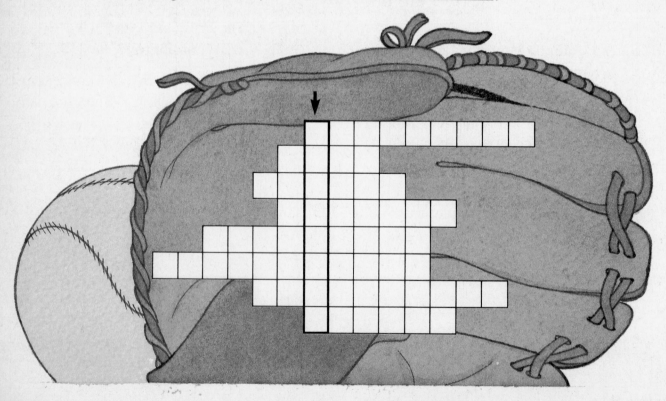

Name _____   Date _____

Thank You, Jackie Robinson

● Think about the story "Thank You,
Jackie Robinson." Below are the names of
five things in the story. Tell how each thing
was important.

1. Ebbets Field _____

_____

_____

_____

2. subway map _____

_____

_____

_____

3. dugout _____

_____

_____

_____

4. ticket stub _____

_____

_____

5. ballpoint pen _____

_____

_____

_____

Name _____   Date _____

Almanac

- Below are sample excerpts from an almanac. Study the excerpts. Then answer the questions, using information from both excerpts.

PRESIDENTS OF THE UNITED STATES

Name of President	Term in Office	Date and Place Born	Died	Age Died
7. Jackson	1829-1837	3/15/1767 – South Carolina	6/8/1845	78
8. Van Buren	1837-1841	12/5/1782 – New York	7/24/1862	79
9. Harrison, W.H.	*1841	2/9/1773 – Virginia	4/4/1841	68
*Died in office.				

PRESIDENTIAL BIOGRAPHIES

William Henry Harrison was born in Virginia on Feb. 9, 1773. He joined the army in 1791, became secretary of the Northwest Territory in 1798, and governor of Indiana in 1800. He married Anna Symmes in 1795. After retiring from the army in 1814, he went into politics. He ran for President in 1836 against Van Buren, but lost. He was elected in 1840 but caught pneumonia and died one month after taking office.

1. When and where was Jackson born? _____

2. Who was the eighth President? _____

3. How old was Van Buren when he died? _____

4. Which President was born in Virginia? _____

5. What does the asterisk beside 1841 mean? _____

6. What was W.H. Harrison's middle name? _____

7. What did Harrison do in 1814? _____

_____

8. Whom did Harrison marry? _____

9. For how long did Harrison serve as President? _____

10. What caused Harrison's death? _____

Name _____   Date _____

Getting Information from a Newspaper

- Suppose that your local newspaper ran these articles. Read each one carefully. Then read the questions. Circle the letter of the correct answer to each question. For the starred item, mark the space for the answer.

WATER MAIN BREAKS DOWNTOWN
By Jud Felson

BOSTON (AP) — Traffic was brought to a standstill yesterday when a wall of water crashed down Elm Street. One of the oldest and largest water pipes in the city broke at noon. Mayor Johnson ordered the fire department to rescue people in nearby buildings. The water in the streets was so high that messengers used canoes to get through. Traffic was backed up for miles. By nightfall, the area was cleaned up and traffic, normal.

1. What section of the newspaper would contain this story?
   - **a.** classified   **c.** sports
   - **b.** editorials   **d.** front page
2. What name appears in the by-line?
   - **a.** Mayor Johnson   **c.** Jud Felson
   - **b.** messengers   **d.** fire department
3. When did this event take place?
   - **a.** yesterday at noon   **c.** tomorrow
   - **b.** today at noon   **d.** night
4. What is this story about?
   - **a.** fire rescue   **c.** water-main break
   - **b.** canoes   **d.** traffic
5. What is the dateline of this story?
   - **a.** Boston   **c.** Elm Street
   - **b.** the suburbs   **d.** nearby buildings
6. Which news service provided the story?
   - **a.** UPI   **c.** AP
   - **b.** Elm   **d.** IB

JEFFERSON SETS WORLD RECORD
By Kevin Maltby

LONDON (UPI) — American high jumper, Joan Jefferson, soared to a new world record last night. She cleared six feet six inches, beating Dana Hill by an inch. Jumping Joan's coach, Teddy Salem, said Jefferson managed to avoid all the problems she had the day before. Jefferson, still suffering from an ankle injury she got last month in Berlin, plans to compete in two more events before the meet ends tomorrow at the stadium.

7. In what section of the newspaper would this story be likely to appear?
   - **a.** classified   **c.** sports
   - **b.** editorials   **d.** front page
8. What name appears in the by-line?
   - **a.** Joan Jefferson   **c.** Dana Hill
   - **b.** Kevin Maltby   **d.** Teddy Salem
9. When did this event take place?
   - **a.** last month   **c.** the day before
   - **b.** last night   **d.** today
10. What was this story about?
    - **a.** ankle injury   **c.** problems
    - **b.** new world record   **d.** Teddy Salem
11. What is the dateline of this event?
    - **a.** London   **c.** Berlin
    - **b.** the stadium   **d.** America

★ Which news service provided the story?
   - ○ AP
   - ○ six feet six inches
   - ○ UPI
   - ○ ET

Name _____ Date _____

Getting Information from a Newspaper

● Suppose that the index at the right appeared in your newspaper. Read each question. Write the letter of the section and the number or numbers of the pages where you would find the answer. The first one has been done for you. For the starred item, mark the space for the answer.

Today's Index

Arnie's Answers A35-36
Business D1-7
Classified B8-13
Comics B16
Crossword C7
Editorials A17-18
Entertainment B11-15
Living C1-5
Sports D14-20
TV/Radio C8
Weather C9

_____C8_____ 1. Are there any movies being shown on TV at 9:00 P.M.?

_____ 2. Are there any used bikes for sale?

_____ 3. Is the weekend going to be fair and sunny?

_____ 4. Who won the national finals of the hockey tournament?

_____ 5. What are the critics saying about the new play that just opened?

_____ 6. How much snow fell east of the Rocky Mountains last night?

_____ 7. How did the high cost of heating fuels affect local businesses?

_____ 8. How can you brighten up a small, dark room?

_____ 9. What did newspaper readers think of the article on taxes last week?

_____ 10. Did the reviewer like the new book, *Autumn Leaves*?

_____ 11. How much would a vacation house in the mountains cost?

_____ 12. What time will the President's radio address be aired?

_____ 13. Are there any good vegetable recipes in the paper today?

_____ 14. What did Arnie's Answers say about smoke alarms in homes?

_____ 15. Are there any jobs available for carpenters?

_____ 16. What is happening to Charlie Brown in the "Peanuts" comic strip today?

_____ 17. Are there any inexpensive station wagons for sale?

_____ 18. What do the editors think of this new law on toxic wastes?

★ Who won the big game at the stadium last night?
   ○ D1 – 7   ○ B8 – 13
   ○ B11 – 15   ○ D14 – 20

Name _____ Date _____

Topic and Main Idea

• Read the article. Then follow the directions below.

(1) The most important loggers in the forests of Thailand are elephants. They roll huge logs through the brush and use their trunks to lift them into rivers for transport. Adult elephants can carry as much as six hundred pounds on their backs. In some forests, modern logging vehicles have replaced the beasts. Yet elephants will probably log for many years to come, for they can traverse steep and narrow paths that weighty vehicles cannot enter.

(2) The government of Thailand has its own school — with teachers called *mahouts* — to train elephants for logging. When young animals first come to the training center, they are untamed and wild. They need to be constrained within a wooden cell, tight enough so the elephant cannot injure itself by thrashing. When the elephant calms down, its newly-elected

mahout feeds it a juicy treat of forest leaves. In the days to come, the *mahout* will train his elephant with patience and care. Punishing or striking an elephant is never allowed.

(3) The bond between an elephant and its *mahout* forms over time. The *mahouts* stay with their elephants throughout their working lives. An amazing bond of trust, even love, is formed between the *mahout* and his elephant. Signs of great distress have been witnessed in an elephant if its *mahout* has to leave it for some reason. It may suffer severe loss of appetite or become listless and ill. One elephant was even said to have wept real tears at a rebuke from its *mahout*!

1. Write the topic of each paragraph on the lines below.

(1) _____ (3) _____

(2) _____

2. Write the main idea of each paragraph above.

(1) _____

(2) _____

(3) _____

3. Write the main idea of the entire article. _____

_____

Name _____ **Date** _____

Idioms

Guided Practice

_____ **1.** The entries for the contest were due at noon, and I was lucky to get mine in **under the wire.**

    a. barely in time   **b.** below the fence   **c.** too late

_____ **2.** Luther was **down at the mouth** when he lost the game.

    a. hungry   **b.** happy   **c.** unhappy

_____ **3.** I want to get an unusual gift, but these things are **run-of-the-mill.**

    a. made from flour   **b.** unusual   **c.** ordinary

4. "Hi, Mitchell. You looked **burned up**. Are you upset?"

_____

5. "Yes. If I tell you the reason, will you keep it **under your hat?"** _____

6. "Sure, Mitchell. I can keep a secret. **My lips are sealed.**"

_____

7. "It's Kenneth. This morning I asked him a simple question, and he **jumped down my throat**. It was hard to quiet him

down." _____

8. "Mitchell, you'll never get Kenneth to change his ways. You

might as well **throw in the towel**." _____

9. "I guess you're right. But unless Kenneth stops **acting up**, he'll

regret his behavior." _____

Name _____ **Date** _____

Idioms

● Read each sentence. The underlined word is an idiom. Choose the best meaning of the idiom. Circle the letter of your answer. For the starred item, mark the space for the answer.

1. Whenever Ryan is <u>under the weather</u>, he gets plenty of rest and takes vitamins.
   a. out in the rain   **b.** ill   **c.** exercising

2. Mario's jokes <u>wear thin</u> after you've heard them ten times.
   a. become dull   **b.** become shorter   **c.** remain funny

3. I like my neighborhood to look clean, so it <u>burns me up</u> when I see someone littering on the street.
   a. makes me feel hot   **b.** makes me angry   **c.** starts fires

4. Walking in the woods, we saw a rabbit appear <u>out of the blue</u>.
   a. from a hole   **b.** unexpectedly   **c.** running fast

5. Josie likes hockey so much that she'll play the game <u>at the drop of a hat</u>.
   a. when she can   **b.** if a hat is dropped   **c.** using a hat

6. Although Andy did well in the spelling bee, he <u>tripped up</u> when he came to the word *giraffe*.
   a. fell on the floor   **b.** made a mistake   **c.** spoke quietly

7. Although Darryl didn't like the new plan, he went along with it because he hated to <u>make waves</u>.
   a. cause trouble   **b.** go swimming   **c.** talk loudly

 That movie was so funny; it really had me <u>in stitches</u>.

   ○ sewing
   ○ laughing hard
   ○ at the doctor's office
   ○ watching eagerly

Name _____   Date _____

Comprehension: Understanding Idioms

The Gorillagram

- Each word in the box is defined in one of the sentences. Choose the word that completes each definition and write it in the sentence.

chorus	technicalities
poised	manufacturer
	rainspout

1. A metal drainpipe that carries water from the roof of a building to the ground is called a _____.

2. Someone who makes products in a factory is a _____.

3. To remain in one spot, as if suspended, is to be _____.

4. A _____ is a group of singers or dancers who perform together.

5. _____ are small details that can keep you from dealing with the important things about a subject.

- Use the words from the box to complete the sentences.

1. The conductor stood _____ in front of the _____ ready to give the signal to sing.

2. The _____ of the bicycles said that the company would replace any parts that were not perfect.

3. Water was not draining properly from the roof because the _____ was stuffed with leaves.

4. Although Marie played a wonderful game of tennis, she was disqualified because of two _____.

Name _____ Date _____

The Gorillagram

- Think about the story "The Gorillagram."
Complete the news article below by writing
one word from the box on each blank line.

party	manufacturer	act	gorilla
moon	ladder	dog	father
canoe	originators	roof	school
noise	rainspout	suit	police

★ ★ ★ ≡   **The Gorillagram Girls Plus One**   ≡ ★ ★ ★

Several days ago, this newspaper reported an incident that occurred last Saturday at a local _____. Involved in the incident were Jan Peabody and her friend Barbara, _____ of the now-famous Gorillagram. Jan and Barbara started the Gorillagram business in order to raise money for a _____ trip. Last Saturday afternoon, they were on their way to a _____, dressed in their _____ suits. As they crossed the schoolyard, they encountered a stray _____, who was apparently frightened by the suits. When the dog charged, the girls dashed to the school building and scooted up a _____ to the safety of the _____. The dog caught Jan

in the seat of the pants and ripped her _____. The dog — whom Jan named Herbert — held the girls prisoner until late that evening. Then, when the _____ rose, the dog started howling. The _____ resulted in a complaint from someone in the neighborhood. _____ arrived and rescued the girls by _____.

The Gorillagram girls are still in business — but with a difference. Jan Peabody has adopted Herbert and plans to use him in the _____. The ruined gorilla suit, which had been rented from Jan's _____, has been replaced with money from the _____ of the rainspout. The manufacturer is using the girls' picture in an ad!

Name _____ Date _____

Locating Information Quickly

● Skim the title, subtitles, and first and last sentences of the article to find the topic. Write it on the line. Then read each question. Scan the article to answer the question. Write the letter of the paragraph in which the answer is found.

Topic: _____

_____

_____

____ 1. What Native American foods did the settlers learn to eat?

____ 2. What goods couldn't the settlers make in the wilds?

____ 3. What did the typical colonial house look like?

____ 4. Where was the first permanent English settlement?

____ 5. What were some foods that made up the old English diet?

Early Settlers

A. The First Permanent Settlement

Unlike the explorers, the early settlers were not looking for treasure or for trade. They planned instead to live and to work in this new wilderness. In 1620, the first permanent settlement was established in Jamestown, Virginia, which is on the Atlantic Coast.

B. Importing Goods

At first, the settlers knew little about life in the wild. Many tried to keep their old English customs by importing goods that could not be made in the wilderness. Clothing, tools, and ammunition had to be brought specially and preserved while the first farming and building began. This produced much hardship and forced the settlers to depend on England for assistance.

C. Food

Living in the wilderness changed the settlers' way of eating. Instead of eating beef and bread, they learned to eat many native American foods, such as corn, beans, pumpkin, berries, and turkey. Later, the settlers grew crops brought from Europe, including wheat and barley.

D. Clothing and Shelter

Clothing and shelter for the early settlers was a mixture of old and new. When their European clothes wore out, the settlers replaced them with leather and fur. At first, the settlers lived in tents and caves. Later, they made English-style cottages from logs and outside planks called clapboards. The typical house was square. It had a single room and a large fireplace used for cooking and heating.

Name _____ **Date** _____

Sequence • Events and Clue Words

Guided Practice

A. Paper, as we know it, is a mixture of wood, plant fibers, and rags. It is said that the ancient Chinese discovered the art of paper making after watching wasps make paperlike nests of a combination of old wood and tough plant fibers. Several ancient Chinese paper makers were captured in a battle in what is now part of the Soviet Union. Encouraged to continue their profession in prison, these paper makers taught others who later made the art known in Spain and, eventually, in all of Europe. From 1750 to 1882, various inventions improved the art of paper making until the process became similar to that used today.

_____ The Chinese taught the art of paper making to others.

_____ Several ancient Chinese paper makers were captured.

_____ Paper making was made known in Spain.

_____ Wasps made nests of wood and plant fibers.

_____ Ancient Chinese learned to make paper.

_____ Inventions improved the art of paper making.

B. Before Milly left for the library, she grabbed her umbrella. She had gone to the store earlier in the day and had gotten soaked in a sudden downpour. She didn't want that to happen again. As Milly was walking to the library, it started to rain once more. She tried to open the umbrella, but it broke right in her hand. Milly got soaked again!

1. _____

2. _____

3. _____

4. _____

5. _____

6. _____

Name _____ **Date** _____

Sequence • Events and Clue Words

● Read this short biography of a famous doctor, Hideyo Noguchi. Pay careful attention to the order, or sequence, of the events in Dr. Noguchi's life. Then read the questions. Circle the letter of each correct answer. For the starred item, mark the space for the answer.

Hideyo Noguchi was born in 1876 in Japan. As an infant, he received a severe burn. However, the Noguchi family was poor and couldn't afford a doctor for the child. As a result, his left hand became paralyzed and deformed.

Not until Noguchi was in his early teens did he go to a clinic where he was operated on by Dr. Kane Watanabe. The operation and a series of treatments eventually brought back motion to the boy's thumb and little finger. To repay Dr. Watanabe, Noguchi worked summers at the clinic. During this time, he saw the suffering of many patients and began to think about the possibility of helping them.

While working at the clinic, Noguchi read all the doctor's medical books. Then he went to a missionary who taught him English, so he could read more medical books. Noguchi worked, studied, and saved his money to go to the medical school in Tokyo. When he got there, he took a job as a janitor to support himself. Eventually, after much work, he received his degree.

In 1900, Dr. Noguchi came to America, where he did research on snake venoms. He later wrote an outstanding book on this topic. As a staff member of the Rockefeller Institute for Medical Research, he spent many years studying the causes of diseases. In 1928, while studying yellow fever in Africa, he caught the disease and died.

1. Which of these events happened first?
   a. Noguchi's hand was operated on.
   b. Noguchi's hand was burned and deformed.
   c. Noguchi regained use of his hand.

2. Which of these events happened before Noguchi went to Tokyo?
   a. Noguchi learned English.
   b. Noguchi went to medical school.
   c. Noguchi studied snake venom.

3. Which of these events happened while Noguchi was in medical school?
   a. He wrote a book on snake venoms.
   b. He worked on the staff of the Rockefeller Institute for Research.
   c. He worked as a janitor.

★ Which of these events happened last?
   ○ Noguchi got his medical degree.
   ○ Noguchi went to Africa.
   ○ Noguchi read more medical books.
   ○ Noguchi did research on snakes.

Name _____ Date _____

Comprehension: Noting Correct Sequence — Events and Clue Words   Unit 13 • CELEBRATIONS

The Mural

● Find the word that goes with each definition in the row or column of the puzzle with the same number. Circle the word in the puzzle. Then write it on the line below the definition.

ACROSS

1. Traditions handed down from one generation to another.

_____

2. Obligations.

_____

3. An Indian people of central Mexico noted for their advanced civilization.

_____

DOWN

4. An American of Mexican heritage.

_____

5. A painting on a wall.

_____

6. A member of the people of Central America and Southern Mexico whose Civilization peaked in A.D. 1000.

_____

```
      4       5         6
    C O R T E Z O P A I N T
  1 H E R I T A G E B L U E T
    I N E Z I G O N P A R K Y
  2 C O M M I T M E N T S K Y
    A Q U A T L A L V A T O S
    N U R O C S Y M B O L S T
  3 O I A L A M A Z T E C T D
    S A L E C O N T E S T D
```

Name _____   Date _____

The Mural

● Think about the story "The Mural." On the first blank in each item, write the name of a character listed in the box. Then complete the sentence.

Mercedes	**Mr. Alva**
Abuelita	**Inez**

1. _____ painted a picture of the history of Mexico.

   It showed _____

   _____

   _____

2. _____ painted a picture of Mexico's future.

   It showed _____

   _____

3. _____ took Inez and Mercedes to see the wall

   the girls were to paint. He had put up a barricade so that _____

   _____

   _____

4. When _____ saw that Inez had painted the sun

   peeking from behind a skyscraper, she was upset because _____

   _____

   _____

5. _____ understood Mercedes' feelings about

   having to share everything with Inez, and she promised to _____

   _____

   _____

Name _____ Date _____

Using Context

● Read the story. The underlined words are listed at the bottom of the page with three possible meanings. Circle the letter of the correct meaning for the word as it is used in the story.

Chris was so [1]indecisive. He couldn't make up his mind what shirt to wear, much less what to do for a science project.

[2]Initially Chris had decided to build a [3]miniature space station, but he quickly [4]abandoned that idea. Working with all those tiny pieces would take too much of his time.

Next, he decided to do an experiment that would prove microwaves were [5]detrimental to people's health. That did not seem like such a good idea either, because Chris didn't know how to do it without harming his own health.

Then he decided to collect fossils because he already had two of them. Chris quickly gave up that idea also. Being able to find fossils in the winter was far too [6]tentative. He certainly couldn't submit a collection of only two fossils!

"What am I going to do," [7]wailed Chris, almost in tears, when his mother came to see him.

"Why not show the bad effects of loud noises?" asked his mother.

"How can I do that?" asked Chris.

"You've got everything you need right here," his mom responded. "Look at your plants — the ones that are exposed to that [8]raucous noise you call music. They are all dying. My plants — the ones that get soft, pretty music — are all healthy. Just start new plants and give them the same amount of the different kinds of music each day and see how they do."

"Great idea, Mom. I'll start right away," said Chris, turning up his stereo.

His mother covered her ears with her hands and left Chris's room as quickly as she could.

1. **indecisive**	a. not kind	b. not able to decide	c. not polite
2. **initially**	a. at first	b. forever	c. finally
3. **miniature**	a. huge	b. a small copy	c. a full-size copy
4. **abandoned**	a. started	b. finished	c. gave up
5. **detrimental**	a. healthful	b. harmful	c. not important
6. **tentative**	a. sure	b. uncertain	c. cruel
7. **wailed**	a. cried	b. shouted	c. answered
8. **raucous**	a. soothingly quiet	b. irritatingly loud	c. musically pleasing

Name _____ Date _____

Commas

● Read each sentence and the statements below it. Decide which statements agree with the meaning of the sentence. Write **Yes** before each statement that agrees with the meaning. Write **No** before each statement that does not agree. The first set has been done for you.

1. Paul, Mary Lou, Carlos, Johnny, and Mary Jane, the class president, all met at the school-reunion party.

    __No__ Seven students met at the party.

    __Yes__ Mary Jane is the class president.

    __Yes__ Five students met at the party.

2. "If you want this dog, Willie, Bob," Jan said, "you must take him for walks, give him baths, and feed him often."

    _____ The dog's name is Willie.

    _____ Jan told Willie to care for Bob.

    _____ Jan told Bob how to take care of Willie.

3. When Harold first met Sarah, his cousin, and her children, Jan, Kevin, and Jerry, he was happier than ever.

    _____ Sarah met Harold and a cousin.

    _____ Kevin is one of Sarah's children.

    _____ Sarah has three children.

4. Sam said his favorite movie, *Tess Tobias,* set in England, was very scenic.

    _____ Sam was talking to Tess Tobias.

    _____ *Tess Tobias* is a scenic movie.

    _____ Tess was the one speaking.

5. "Paul, can Karen, my friend and a good shot, join our game?" asked Tom.

    _____ Tom asked Karen a question.

    _____ Tom wanted to ask three friends to play.

    _____ Tom asked permission to invite only one friend to play.

6. Ms. Mitchell, my neighbor, sent us apples, nuts, and a mango, the reddish-yellow tropical fruit.

    _____ My neighbor is saying something to Ms. Mitchell.

    _____ One tropical fruit is the mango.

    _____ Ms. Mitchell is my neighbor.

7. Whenever I sleep late, my dog Buffy wakes me up.

    _____ Buffy sometimes sleeps late.

    _____ Buffy is the name of a dog.

    _____ Someone is talking to Buffy.

8. "If you can, John, call Joe," Tom said, "and ask about Peter, his brother."

    _____ John was speaking to Joe.

    _____ Joe's brother is Peter.

    _____ Tom was speaking to Joe.

Name _____ Date _____

Predicting Outcomes

Guided Practice

A. As a beginning skier, Mike was not aware that all snowy surfaces are not equally good for skiing. He didn't know that powdery or coarse-grained snow is generally safe but half-melted, refrozen snow is extremely dangerous. He thought that whenever there was snow on the ground, it was time to head for the slopes. So, after a week of warm weather followed by freezing cold, Mike decided to go skiing.

____ Mike went skiing and had a wonderful time.

____ Mike went skiing and fell down a lot.

____ Mike thought it over and decided not to ski after all.

B. Going up in the ski lift, Mike met a man who had been skiing for many years, well enough to win several championships. The man asked Mike how long he had been skiing. When Mike said he was still just learning to ski, his new friend seemed very surprised.

"You must be a very daring skier," he said, "to go out on these slopes in the condition they are in today."

Mike looked down at the inviting white surfaces below him. "They look in great condition to me," he said.

The man explained how dangerous they could be when the snow had thawed and refrozen. Looking at Mike's worried face, he concluded, "There's a big fire in the fireplace back at the ski lodge. I understand they're showing a good movie this afternoon, too, about the basics of safe skiing."

_____

_____

_____

_____

Name _____ **Date** _____

Predicting Outcomes

• Read each part of the story, looking for clues to help predict the outcome. Then answer the questions. Put an **X** on the line before each correct answer. For the starred part, mark the spaces for the answers.

Sarah had always been afraid of diving from the high board. To join the school swimming team, however, she had to dive from this board. So every afternoon, her older brother, Tim, helped her practice her diving.

On the day of the try-outs, Sarah felt a little nervous. Joining the team was important to her. She climbed the ladder slowly. At the top, she looked down and saw her brother. Tim smiled and Sarah relaxed. She walked to the edge of the board.

1. What do you predict happened next?

_____ She decided not to dive.

_____ She dove into the water.

_____ She fell into the water.

2. Which clue helped you decide?

_____ Sarah felt a little nervous.

_____ She climbed to the ladder slowly.

_____ Tim smiled and Sarah relaxed.

★ As Sarah rose up to dive, a big truck backfired. The sudden loud noise startled Sarah so much that she jumped, lost her balance, and fell into the water. She was so embarrassed that she wished she could stay at the bottom of the pool. As she rose to the surface, however, the coach put out her hand to help Sarah out of the pool. "Those trucks should be banned from this road," said the coach. "Do you want to try again?"

1. What do you predict will happen?
○ Sarah will not get on the team.
○ Sarah will try the dive again.
○ Sarah will never swim again.
○ The trucks will be banned.

2. Which clue helped you decide?
○ Sarah was so embarrassed.
○ The noise had startled her too much.
○ The coach helped her out of the pool.
○ The coach offered her another try.

Name _____ Date _____

Home from School

● Read each sentence. Find the meaning that fits the underlined word. Write the word next to its meaning.

1. Although my aunt has <u>cerebral palsy</u>, she gets along very well in her wheelchair.
2. John appeared <u>sheepish</u> as he examined the vase he'd broken.
3. Most people would have felt embarrased by the situation, but Paul was <u>unabashed</u>.
4. Ed's leg <u>braces</u> allow him more freedom than his wheelchair.
5. The horse never <u>faltered</u> when it came to the high fence; it just jumped right over it.
6. The scientist worked <u>doggedly</u> on her experiment all through the night.
7. Alice enjoyed being a <u>therapist</u> because she was able to help so many people.
8. Assembling a 5000-piece jigsaw puzzle was a <u>complicated</u> job.

_____ Medical devices used to support parts of the body.

_____ Not giving up easily; stubbornly.

_____ Someone who treats a disease or physical disorder.

_____ Embarrassed and apologetic.

_____ Not easy to understand or deal with; perplexing.

_____ Weakness or lack of muscular coordination resulting from brain damage, usually at birth.

_____ Not embarrassed or abashed.

_____ Lost strength or momentum; hesitated.

● Write sentences using three of the underlined words.

_____

_____

_____

_____

_____

Name _____ Date _____

Home from School

● Think about the story "Home from
School." Circle the best answer to each
question below. Then write a reason for
your choice.

1. How did Sally feel about her new room?

     indifferent   delighted   displeased

_____

_____

_____

2. How did Sally feel when Meg asked why she wore leg braces?

     calm   indifferent   uncomfortable

_____

_____

_____

3. How did Sally feel when she was left alone to dress?

     uncomfortable   afraid   calm

_____

_____

4. How did Sally feel as she dressed herself?

     angry   determined   embarrassed

_____

_____

5. How did Sally's family feel when they saw her all dressed?

     admiring   embarrassed   uncomfortable

_____

_____

Name _____ Date _____

Idioms

● Read each sentence. Use the context to figure out the meaning of the underlined idiom. Then write a meaning for the idiom that can take its place in the sentence. The first one has been done for you.

1. After waiting on line for an hour, Byron got fed up and decided to skip the movie. _tired_____

2. When she got an A on the test, Randy was on cloud nine.

   _____

3. Stan rarely gets angry, but he really flew off the handle when his team lost. _____

4. The students were eager to put on a class play, so they were very happy when Ms. Bond gave them the green light.

   _____

5. In the election for class president, Toby and Lee were neck and neck. _____

6. Though usually fearless, the explorers got cold feet and didn't climb the cliff. _____

7. Although Marlon liked football, by early March he got the itch to take out his baseball mitt. _____

8. Bob and Alejandro made plans to meet at noon, and Alejandro arrrived on the button. _____

9. Patti had hoped to make money with her lemonade stand, but after two days she was in the red. _____

10. Jack tried to catch Susie's eye, but Susie was working so hard that she didn't see anything. _____

Name _____ Date _____

Taking Tests

- Read the article.

Color in Light

Where do colors come from? In a funny way, rainbows hold the answer. Rainbows are caused by sunlight passing through tiny raindrops in the air after rainstorms. The mist in the air breaks up the white light into different colors.

There are other ways to break up, or refract, light. Pieces of large cut glass called *prisms* are often placed by windows so that sunlight shining through them will be split apart. Each small rainbow created is exactly like the rainbows we see in the sky. Scientists use prisms to study colors.

The colors we see in light are made from some combination of three primary colors: red, blue, and green. For example, an orange light is a mixture of red and green light. A purple light is a mixture of red and blue.

The objects around us have color because light bounces off their surfaces in different ways. Green grass absorbs all other colors and lets our eyes see only the green. Apples are red for the same reason. In dark rooms, most objects seem dull and gray. So, in a way, color is really just light.

- Read each question. Mark the space for the answer.

1. Of the following colors, which one is a primary color?
   ○ brown   ○ orange   ○ blue   ○ violet

2. What are prisms?
   ○ mist   ○ special kinds of paints   ○ dusty clouds   ○ pieces of cut glass

3. What does sunlight pass through to create a rainbow?
   ○ tiny raindrops   ○ objects around us   ○ shady areas   ○ bands of light

- Are the statements true or false? Mark the spaces for the answers.

4. Without light bouncing off objects, there would be no color.   ○ True   ○ False

5. Purple, orange, and brown are all primary colors.   ○ True   ○ False

★ What should you do when you are finished with a test? Mark the space for the answer.
○ Make wild guesses at answers you didn't know.
○ Hand the test to the teacher immediately.
○ Check your answers for careless mistakes.
○ Change any answers you weren't sure of.

Name _____   Date _____

Getting Information from a Newspaper

● Each numbered item would be found in a different section of a newspaper. The sections are listed in the box. Decide the section that would contain each item. Write the name of the section on the line beside the item. The first one has been done for you.

Ask Amy	**TV/Radio**	**Living**	**Weather**
Classified	**Editorials**	**Sports**	**Entertainment**
Crossword	**Business**		

1. The Rodney Corporation recently decided to move its factory to Idaho.   Business

2. ATTENTION SKIERS! 15 mins. to Winterville Mountain. This cabin sleeps 10 comfortably. $120/wk. 779-4567

3. If you want to see a great performance of a great play, then I recommend you see the Watertown Players this weekend.

4. I think our senators in Washington should be chosen on the basis of their talents, not on the basis of their bank accounts.

5. After five tries, the Comets finally defeated the Huskies last night before a crowd of 14,000 in the stadium.

6. Paint your house early this fall. Home repairs are a must as you prepare for winter.

7. 6:00 P.M. Wendy's Workout
6:30 P.M. 1982 (movie) "Going to the Stars"
8:30 P.M. (rerun) "Sunny Days"

8. Dear Amy: My parents won't let me stay up past 10:00 P.M. Help!   NO SLEEPYHEAD
Dear No Sleepyhead: Sweet Dreams!

9. The forecast for Friday is cold with increasing cloudiness and rain.

10. **7 DOWN** A seven-letter word for funny.
10 DOWN In the heat of the ____ .

Name _____ Date _____

Maps

Guided Practice

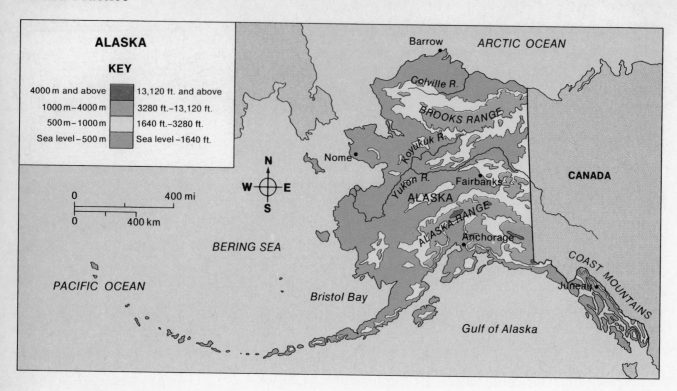

_____ **1.** This map shows the major products of Alaska.

_____ **2.** This map shows the height of land areas in Alaska.

_____ **3.** You can tell the capital city on this map.

---

4. What is the elevation of the land around Nome?

_____

5. Which mountain range has the highest elevation?

_____

6. Is the Brooks Range in the northern or southern part of Alaska?

_____

7. What is the elevation of the land along the western coast of Alaska?

_____

8. How many rivers are shown on the map?

_____

Name _____ **Date** _____

Maps

Guided Practice

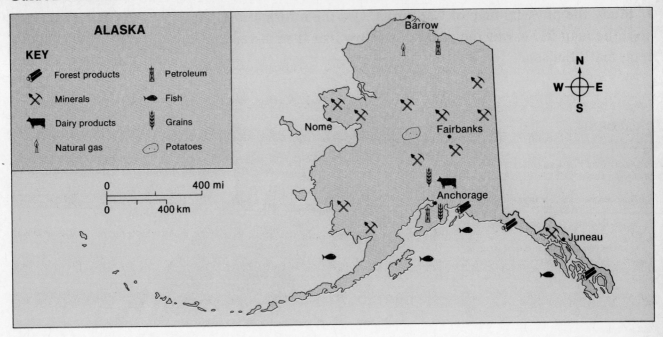

_____ 1. This map shows the major mountain ranges in Alaska.

_____ 2. This map shows the countries bordering Alaska.

_____ 3. This map shows the major products of Alaska.

---

4. What is the symbol for minerals?

_____

5. What does the symbol 🪵 stand for?

_____

6. What symbol shows where petroleum is found?

_____

7. Along which coast is fishing most important?

_____

8. What vegetable is grown in Alaska?

_____

9. Where are most of Alaska's minerals found?

_____

Name _____ **Date** _____

Maps

- Study the physical map of California. Use the information from the map to answer the questions below. For the starred item, mark the space for the answer.

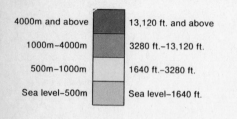

CALIFORNIA

KEY

4000m and above	13,120 ft. and above
1000m–4000m	3280 ft.–13,120 ft.
500m–1000m	1640 ft.–3280 ft.
Sea level–500m	Sea level–1640 ft.

0   100   200   300 mi
0   100   200   300 km

1. What does the color green show? _____

2. What does the color yellow show? _____

_____

3. What color shows land higher than 13,120 feet above sea level? _____

4. What is the elevation of the land around Sacramento? _____

_____

5. What mountain range has the highest elevation? _____

6. In what part of the state are the Sierra Nevadas? _____

★ What is the elevation of the land in the Mojave Desert?
  ○ sea level to 1640 feet   ○ 1640 to 3280 feet
  ○ 3280 to 13,120 feet   ○ 13,120 feet and above

Name _____ **Date** _____

Maps

● Study the product map of California. Use the information from the map to answer the questions below. For the starred item, mark the space for the answer.

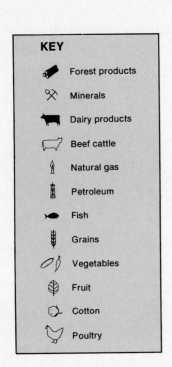

KEY

Forest products

Minerals

Dairy products

Beef cattle

Natural gas

Petroleum

Fish

Grains

Vegetables

Fruit

Cotton

Poultry

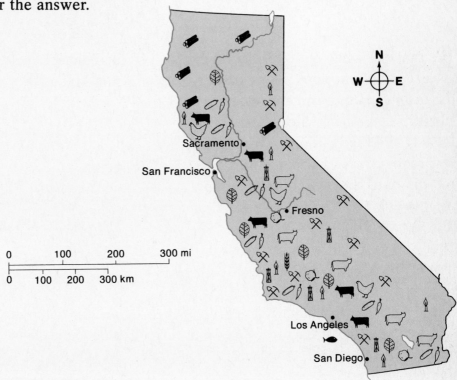

0   100   200   300 mi
0   100 200 300 km

1. What symbol is used for forest products? _____

2. What symbol is used for poultry? _____

3. What does the symbol 🍃 stand for? _____

4. In what area of the state are most forest products found? _____

_____

5. Which is grown in more areas — grain or vegetables? _____

6. Where is California's fishing industry located? _____

7. What kind of farms are found just south of Sacramento? _____

★ What is grown just west of Fresno?
   ○ fruit   ○ vegetables   ○ cotton   ○ grains

Name _____   **Date** _____

Taming the West

● Read each paragraph and the words at the right. Circle the letter of the word that correctly completes the sentence with the blank.

The ranger looked out over the forest. It was a scorching hot day. There hadn't been a drop of rain in three weeks. It was the perfect ___1___ in which a forest fire could start and rage out of control quickly.

1. **a.** colony   **b.** environment
    c. settlement   **d.** palace

The ranger raised her binoculars and looked out over the range, first ___2___ and then westward. There was no sign of trouble yet.

2. **a.** up   **b.** down
    c. sideways   **d.** eastward

Then she saw it. It was just a tiny puff of smoke, but it meant trouble to a forest ranger. Immediately she got on the phone and reported a fire in the north ___3___.

3. **a.** range   **b.** barn
    c. station   **d.** pole

After calling two firefighters on car patrol, the ranger got into her own firefighting gear and raced down the steps of the tower. She knew the ___4___ procedure well, for she had practiced it often.

4. **a.** equipment   **b.** established
    c. destructive   **c.** daring

Jumping into her jeep, the ranger sped off in the direction of the fire. She hoped that it could be brought under control quickly before it could ___5___ too many trees.

5. **a.** construct   **b.** decrease
    c. destroy   **d.** invent

At the scene of the fire, she joined the other firefighters. They worked for hours spraying the trees and digging a fire line. The task seemed ___6___.

6. **a.** boring   **b.** enjoyable
    c. fascinating   **d.** endless

At last it was over. The firefighters slapped one another on the back. Then they congratulated the ___7___ smoke jumpers who had parachuted into the area to help.

7. **a.** powerful   **b.** sweet
    c. daring   **d.** hopeful

Name _____ Date _____

Taming the West

● Think about the article "Taming the
West." Decide whether each statement is
true or false, and circle that answer. Then
write a reason for your choice.

1. The Pacific Coast section was the last part of the United
   States to be settled.   True   False

   _____

   _____

   _____

2. Winters on the plains were fierce and terrible, but the
   summers were pleasant.   True   False

   _____

   _____

3. Railroads made it easier to settle the plains.
   True   False

   _____

   _____

4. Windmills helped the settlers to get water.
   True   False

   _____

   _____

5. Settlers built miles of wooden fences to keep animals out of
   their planted fields.   True   False

   _____

   _____

Name _____   Date _____

Sequence • Events and Clue Words

● Each sentence tells about two events. Decide whether the underlined event happened before, after, or at the same time as the other event. Put an **X** in the correct column. Circle any clue words that helped you decide on the order. The first one has been done for you.

	Before	After	Same Time
1. We were able to play two more sets of tennis after the weather cleared.	X	___	___
2. The phone rang and rang; finally, someone answered it.	___	___	___
3. Load the film in the camera; then make sure the back is closed tightly.	___	___	___
4. When she scored a *10* for her vault, Mary Lou Retton won an Olympic gold medal in gymnastics.	___	___	___
5. I bought the jeans without trying them on; later, I found they were much too small.	___	___	___
6. Ralph liked running around the school track; previously he had worked out in his backyard.	___	___	___
7. We waited inside the lobby while it rained heavily.	___	___	___
8. Danny tried the puzzle several different ways; finally, he got it right.	___	___	___
9. Paul practiced his lines every day; eventually, he learned his part perfectly.	___	___	___
10. The lights went out right after we saw a bolt of lightning.	___	___	___
11. As Suzanne walked into the room, we all jumped up and yelled, "Surprise!"	___	___	___
12. Maria removed all the books from the shelves; then she dusted the bookcase.	___	___	___
13. Before you hand in your paper, check your answers and be sure your name is on the paper.	___	___	___

Name _____ Date _____

Comprehension: Noting Correct Sequence — Events and Clue Words

Unit 17 • CELEBRATIONS

Topic and Main Idea

Guided Practice

The Miller family encountered many hardships on the journey to their new home. Storms came often and lasted long. Even after the rain stopped, it often left behind raging rivers that the wagon could not cross. Once the family camped for two weeks on the bank of a river while they waited for the swirling waters to go down.

Susannah tried to make the best of things, though she was often uncomfortable and sometimes hungry. She did all she could to help her parents. Many long hours were spent amusing her two small brothers and keeping their spirits up. She found that the activity helped to keep her own spirits up, as well.

The summer edged into autumn, the weather improved, and so did the family's outlook. Father now whistled and sang as he drove the wagon. At night he told jokes and stories. Then came the day when he said the words Susannah had been longing to hear: "Here we are. This will be our new home."

1. _____

2. _____

3. _____

Topic: _____

Main Idea: _____

_____

Detail: _____

How it Supports the Main Idea: _____

_____

Name _____   Date _____

Topic and Main Idea

● Read the story. Then follow the directions.

A. At the last minute, Josie had agreed to take her sister's baby-sitting job with five-year-old Tammy Smith. Josie thought the job would be a breeze. Now, as she walked Tammy to the bowling alley, she was not so sure. "Whoever heard of asking a baby-sitter to take the child bowling?" Josie thought to herself. Yet, that's what Mrs. Smith had asked her to do. Josie had been so shocked by the request that she hadn't asked any questions. She had only said, "Sure, Mrs. Smith." Now, as she walked with Tammy in hand, Josie decided that she'd never again take her sister's jobs!
B. Trouble began almost as soon as Josie and Tammy arrived at the alley. There were no bowling shoes small enough for Tammy. She had to wear shoes that were two sizes too big! When it was time for Tammy to throw the ball, she swung it behind her as she'd seen Josie do. The ball was so heavy that Tammy dropped it — on Josie's toe! Tammy managed to throw the ball in front of her the second time. However, she let it go so softly that it stopped dead in the middle of the lane! Josie blushed deeply when a boy she knew had to walk down the lane to retrieve the ball.
C. By the time Mrs. Smith got home, Tammy was fast asleep. Josie told Mrs. Smith that everything had gone fine. She added that Tammy seemed to enjoy going bowling. Mrs. Smith looked surprised and asked Josie to repeat what she had said. Josie did and received a greater blow than the bowling pins had all night. Mrs. Smith said to her, "Why, Josie, there's been a misunderstanding. I never said to take Tammy to bowl. I said take Tammy *a* bowl — you know, a bowl for her nighttime fruit."

● The paragraphs in the story are lettered **A**, **B**, and **C**. Write the correct letter beside the paragraph topics listed below.

_____ Josie's misunderstanding

_____ Josie's and her sister's baby-sitting job

_____ Josie and Tammy at the bowling alley

★ What is the main idea of the whole story? Mark the space for the answer.
○ Tammy was too young to bowl well.
○ A misunderstanding made Josie's baby-sitting job difficult.
○ Josie became upset while baby-sitting.
○ Josie decided never to take her sister's baby-sitting jobs again.

Name _____ **Date** _____

Cobie's Courage

● Complete the story by writing a word from the box on each blank line.

feverish	scramble	cold	calling	trudged
vanish	hydrophobic	gingerly	blinding	resigned

On a trip to Alaska, I became lost one day in a

_____ snowstorm. The snow was so heavy that I

couldn't see five feet in front of me. My hands and feet were

numb from the _____; I had to keep moving or I

would freeze to death. I was sick and felt hot and

_____, but I knew that if I lay down in the snow no

one would ever find me. I would _____ forever.

As I _____ along, I saw an animal

_____ up a snowbank. It was a timber wolf, and I

hoped it was not _____. Any wild animal can be

dangerous, but meeting a mad one could be fatal. I was almost

_____ to losing my life. But as the wolf

_____ approached, I realized that it was as worried

about me as I was about it. Suddenly, I heard voices

_____ my name, and I knew I was saved.

Name _____   Date _____

Cobie's Courage

- **Think about the story "Cobie's Courage."**
Complete the sentences below.

1. Cobie realized that Mrs. Wiese was lonely because _____
_____

2. Stede and Bedad came to dinner during the winter even
though they did no work because _____
_____

3. Stede and Bedad weren't cold sleeping in a tent because _____
_____

4. Rebecca tried to persuade Cobie that it wasn't necessary to
look for Rachel because _____
_____

5. Cobie was worried about Rachel because _____
_____

6. Rachel couldn't climb out of the well because _____
_____

7. Cobie changed places with Rachel because _____
_____

Name _____ **Date** _____

Predicting Outcomes

● Read each paragraph. After each one, tell what you think will happen to Bobby and why.

1. Bobby sat sadly in the crowded waiting room. He had not seen his family in six months. Now that he had finally planned to go visit them, he had missed his plane. Bobby walked up to the woman at the ticket counter to ask if there was another plane he could take. The woman looked at the boy's drawn face. "I'm sorry," she said, "but I just don't know how I can get you on another plane. They are all full."

_____

_____

2. Bobby waited for three hours, and there were still no seats available on any other planes. He watched as the last happy passengers boarded a plane to his home town. Bobby had just about given up when the ticket agent called out to him: "Wait! There is an empty seat on this plane after all."

_____

_____

3. Snow was falling as Bobby boarded the plane. He found his seat and thought about seeing his family again. Then, a voice came over the loud speaker: "This is your captain, ladies and gentlemen. We are terribly sorry, but because of the weather, we cannot take off right now. We hope the delay will not be lengthy."

_____

_____

Name _____ Date _____

Fact and Opinion

● Read each sentence. If the sentence is a statement of fact, write **F** on the line. If it expresses an opinion, write **O**. If it contains both a fact and an opinion, write **B** and underline the part that expresses an opinion.

_____ 1. The capital of Idaho is Boise.

_____ 2. My sister Molly has three sons.

_____ 3. The spare ribs in Texas taste better than those in New York.

_____ 4. The garage fixes hundreds of cars each week.

_____ 5. James won the last spelling bee, and he will probably win the next one.

_____ 6. Your dog is not nearly as clever as mine.

_____ 7. The country on the United States' southern border is Mexico.

_____ 8. Although Tom has trained two years longer than Jim, he can't sing as well.

_____ 9. In China, most people do not own cars.

_____ 10. In 1920, the polio vaccine had not yet been invented.

_____ 11. My teacher's spelling lesson was really interesting today.

_____ 12. Cairo, which is in Egypt, has the most interesting markets in Africa.

_____ 13. Some glues are made from wheat paste.

_____ 14. It's more fun to play checkers than chess.

_____ 15. The rooftops in Florence are red, which is a more pleasant color than green.

_____ 16. Many states in the United States have names based on American Indian words.

_____ 17. Certain mosquitoes live only three days.

_____ 18. Books about traveling are always too long.

_____ 19. Oahu is one of the many islands that make up the state of Hawaii.

_____ 20. Hank Fisher, the fastest sprinter on our team, plays the trumpet poorly.

_____ 21. Libraries aren't all the same size.

_____ 22. Without a doubt, the best movie ever made was _Old Yeller_.

_____ 23. Argentina is a country in South America whose capital is Buenos Aires.

_____ 24. Our bookstore has thousands of storybooks, although poems are more fun to read.

_____ 25. Soybeans contain many proteins that people need to stay healthy and strong.

_____ 26. Spinach tastes better fresh than cooked.

Name _____ Date _____

Drawing Conclusions

Guided Practice

A. Research into the causes of yellow fever is an interesting medical story. The disease got its name from the effects it has on skin color. In 1881, a Cuban named Carlos Finlay questioned his patients who had yellow fever. He concluded that mosquitoes carried the disease from one person to another. In 1890, American doctors were investigating an outbreak of yellow fever in Cuba. They conducted an experiment by infecting volunteers with yellow fever germs. All but two of them were nursed back to health. The doctors proved that mosquitoes carried the disease.

_____ **1.** Yellow fever made the skin look yellow.

_____ **2.** Carlos Finlay was a doctor.

_____ **3.** Two of the volunteers died from yellow fever.

_____ **4.** Finlay's conclusion about what carried the disease was never actually proved.

B. "Pat, here are some numbers that you may need. The number at the top is where I can be reached.

"Robby is asleep in his crib and should wake up about three o'clock. His bottle is in the refrigerator. Warm it up before giving it to him.

"You must have eaten your lunch, but if you get hungry, help yourself to the fruit in the basket.

"I should be home by five or five-thirty. I know you want to get to the Fourth of July celebration by six P.M. Be sure to lock the door when I leave. Don't let any one in, except Caruso if he meows. Good-by."

1. Yes   No _____

2. Yes   No _____

3. Yes   No _____

4. Yes   No _____

5. Yes   No _____

6. Yes   No _____

Name _____ **Date** _____

Drawing Conclusions

● Read the story and the statements below it. Write **Y** before each statement that can be concluded from the information in the story. Write **N** before each statement that is not supported by the information.

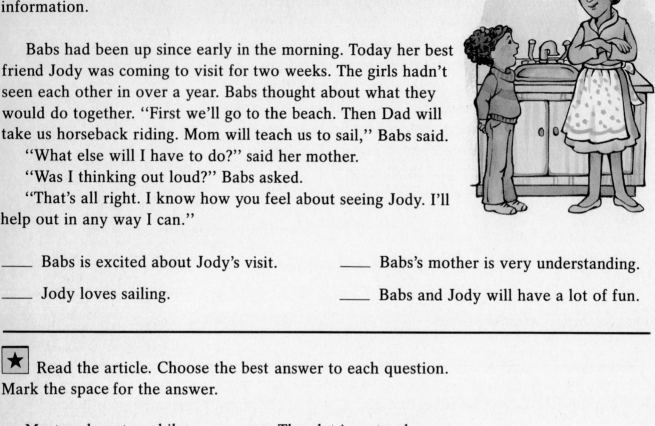

Babs had been up since early in the morning. Today her best friend Jody was coming to visit for two weeks. The girls hadn't seen each other in over a year. Babs thought about what they would do together. "First we'll go to the beach. Then Dad will take us horseback riding. Mom will teach us to sail," Babs said.

"What else will I have to do?" said her mother.

"Was I thinking out loud?" Babs asked.

"That's all right. I know how you feel about seeing Jody. I'll help out in any way I can."

_____ Babs is excited about Jody's visit.   _____ Babs's mother is very understanding.

_____ Jody loves sailing.   _____ Babs and Jody will have a lot of fun.

★ Read the article. Choose the best answer to each question. Mark the space for the answer.

Most early automobiles were open. They let in not only sun, but also wind, rain, and snow. Some had cloth tops and side curtains that could be put up in bad weather, but these fit poorly.

Few roads were paved then, and mud was always a problem. Cars often got stuck in the mud. The riders were often hit by mud splashed up by the wheels. Tires on early cars didn't help cushion the ride either. The tires were filled with a great deal of air, so they were quite hard.

1. What happened to riders in early cars?
   ○ They were protected from weather.
   ○ They never had accidents.
   ○ They got little protection from the weather or mud.
   ○ They enjoyed the excitement of riding a new kind of transportation.

2. What kind of ride did passengers get?
   ○ smooth and quiet
   ○ rough and bumpy
   ○ nice but noisy
   ○ quiet but bumpy

Name _____   Date _____

Escape from NIMH

● Complete the story by writing a word from the box on each blank line.

meekly	plaintive	consternation	concept	astute
maze	anchored	captivity	caution	prime

Paul _____ his boat by the stone wall

bordering the lake. The wall's iron gate was fearsome. Paul

approached the gate and _____ opened it.

Inside, hedgerows guarded a glass house. Paul entered

an opening in the first hedgerow. But the second had three

openings. He tried one, but it was a dead end. To his

_____, the second also led nowhere. "Amazing,"

Paul thought. "Of course!" he shouted. "It's a

_____!"

Grasping the _____, Paul planned how to

reach the house. "But once I'm there, how do I get back?" he said

in a _____ voice.

Then, Paul began unraveling his sweater. He ran through

the maze, making mistakes, trying again, and leaving a trail of

wool. Finally, there was the glass house! As he stepped forward,

a voice roared, "He who dares to enter is a _____

candidate for _____!"

An enormous giant stood before Paul. Grabbing the strand

of wool, Paul ran. When he got home, his mother asked,

"Whatever happened to your sweater?"

Name _____ Date _____

Escape from NIMH

• Think about the story "Escape from NIMH." Write two or three sentences that support each statement below. Use details and events from the story.

1. Even though the cages were comfortable, the rats were unhappy.

_____

_____

_____

_____

2. Jenner was sure Dr. Schultz wouldn't hurt him even if he were caught escaping.

_____

_____

_____

_____

3. Dr. Schultz was excited about the rats' longer life span.

_____

_____

_____

_____

4. Taking the mice along was a good idea.

_____

_____

_____

_____

Name _____ Date _____

Vocabulary

● Read each sentence. Then find the meaning for the underlined word. Mark the space for the answer.

1. The kilt, a kind of skirt, has long been worn by men in Scotland. However, the garment first came from France.
   ○ fabric   ○ word
   ○ piece of clothing   ○ plan

2. Everyone was involved in the school play. Some played roles, while others worked backstage.
   ○ taking part   ○ acting
   ○ absent   ○ watching

3. A rainbow is seen only in the morning or late afternoon. If you see one at 10 A.M. it will vanish before noon.
   ○ get brighter   ○ get larger
   ○ disappear   ○ change

4. Ms. Chan's class was permitted to use the computer every Friday, when students could take turns running programs.
   ○ forbidden   ○ forced
   ○ allowed   ○ unhappy

5. Early American pioneers had no stores that sold clothes. They made some of their clothes from animal hides.
   ○ traders   ○ settlers
   ○ leaders   ○ children

6. This week, our class is reading "Escape from NIMH." The preceding week, we read "Cobie's Courage."
   ○ next   ○ final
   ○ same   ○ earlier

7. Scientists have estimated that the sun will burn out in ten billion years.
   ○ figured out   ○ learned
   ○ decided   ○ hoped

8. Mr. Marks's class had to abandon the idea of visiting a local factory when they learned it had closed down.
   ○ remove   ○ go ahead with
   ○ give up   ○ get together on

9. The fur of the weasel changes color to match its environment. In summer, it is brown; in winter, it is white.
   ○ temperature   ○ air
   ○ surroundings   ○ food

10. In March, the class went on a hike in the woods and tried to detect the first signs of spring.
    ○ exercise   ○ hide
    ○ walk over   ○ discover

11. Benjamin Franklin was a business-person as well as a statesperson. He was one of the first American manufacturers of playing cards.
    ○ makers   ○ enemies
    ○ users   ○ carriers

12. On a typical day at Roosevelt School, class ends at 3 P.M. However, on the day before a holiday, students are let out at noon.
    ○ uncommon   ○ weekly
    ○ usual   ○ rainy

Name _____   Date _____

Taking Tests

- Match the underlined word to its meaning as it is used in the sentence. Mark the space for the answer.

1. Susie is very reliable; you can <u>count</u> on her to be on time.
   ○ a ○ b ○ c ○ d

2. The <u>count</u> did not like it when the king kept him waiting.
   ○ a ○ b ○ c ○ d

3. Jeff's little sister is only three, but she can <u>count</u> to 100.
   ○ a ○ b ○ c ○ d

4. When the final <u>count</u> was in, we knew the President had won by a landslide.
   ○ a ○ b ○ c ○ d

a. to recite numbers
b. to rely upon
c. the total obtained from counting
d. a European noble

- Choose the word that best completes each sentence. Mark the space for the answer.

5. Dad likes driving on country roads more than ____ highways.
   ○ overstate ○ statement ○ interstate

6. There are so few pandas left that they are an ____ species.
   ○ dangerous ○ endanger ○ endangered

7. It is ____ to interrupt when someone is speaking.
   ○ impolite ○ politely ○ politeness

8. Once Luis makes up his mind, he is ____ .
   ○ unchanged ○ unchangeable ○ changing

9. Beth is usually neat, but when she hurries she does things ____ .
   ○ carefully ○ uncareful ○ carelessly

10. Don gets a lot of ____ out of doing things for his friends.
    ○ joyful ○ enjoyable ○ enjoyment

Name _____ Date _____

Punctuation • Points of Ellipsis, Dash, Colon, Semicolon

● Read each paragraph, paying careful attention to the punctuation. Then read the three statements below it. If the statement agrees with the meaning of the paragraph, write **Yes** on the line before the statement. If the statement does not agree with the meaning of the paragraph, write **No.**

1. Over the years Pat had received from Uncle John these rare and colorful pets: snakes, lizards, monkeys, and birds.

_____ Uncle John had sent Pat snakes, lizards, monkeys, and birds.
_____ The snakes, lizards, monkeys, and birds were not colorful pets.
_____ The snakes, lizards, monkeys, and birds were rare and colorful.

2. The most recent packages from Uncle John had stamps from Bangkok, Thailand; Chimbote, Peru; and Sydney, Australia.

_____ Uncle John had sent recent packages from six places.
_____ Uncle John sent packages from three places.
_____ Sydney is in Australia.

3. Last year — a month after Uncle John left on a trip — the express company delivered a package to Pat's house.

_____ The express company delivered a package last year.
_____ The express company delivered a package after Uncle John left.
_____ Uncle John left on a trip a month ago.

4. From the package came a loud squawk; then the words "Stow the chatter" came from inside.

_____ Something inside the package squawked and said, "Stow the chatter."
_____ Pat said, "Stow the chatter" to the package.
_____ *Stow the chatter* was written on the package.

5. As soon as Pat heard those words, he knew that Uncle John — what a terrific uncle — had sent him a parrot.

_____ A terrific uncle other than Uncle John had sent Pat a parrot.
_____ Two uncles had sent a parrot.
_____ Uncle John was terrific.

6. "This house will be too full of animals!" said Pat's mother. She began, "I just don't see . . .," but her voice trailed off as she saw the parrot fly through the kitchen.

_____ The parrot's flight interrupted the words Pat's mother was saying.
_____ Pat's mother walked angrily out of the room.
_____ Pat interrupted his mother.

Name _____   Date _____

Assumptions

Guided Practice

1. ____ Marcie and Paul look alike so they must be sister and brother.

____ Marcie has a pet parakeet that can say ten different things.

2. ____ This bike is better than the other one because this one is more expensive.

____ This bike has a lightweight frame and comes equipped with special racing tires.

3. ____ Cindy reported to the class that she liked the book because it was about horses.

____ Since this book is about horses, Cindy will surely enjoy reading it.

4. The calendar is turned to December already. Next Thursday will be the first day of winter. It will certainly be cold that day.

5. The Wongs must be expecting company. Their porch light is on, and so is the light at the end of their driveway. Both Mr. and Mrs. Wong came home early from work today. Mrs. Wong was carrying a big bag, and Mr. Wong had some flowers.

6.  _____

_____

_____

Name _____ Date _____

Assumptions

Read the sentences in each item. Put an **X** before the
one that contains assumptions. For the starred item,
mark the space for the answer.

1. _____ **a.** Ronnie and Marge plan to ice-skate on Saturday.
   They change into their skates at the rink.

   _____ **b.** During the holidays, the ice-skating rink is open
   every day from noon until 8 P.M.

   _____ **c.** Many people enjoy ice-skating in the winter. Ice-
   skating is the most popular winter sport.

   _____ **d.** Some kinds of ice skates have two blades on each
   skate. Figure skates have one blade on each skate.

2. _____ **a.** Dogs, cats, birds, and fish are common kinds of pets.
   Melissa has a pet dog named Rainey.

   _____ **b.** Melissa is taking Rainey to the veterinarian. A
   veterinarian is an animal doctor.

   _____ **c.** Melissa takes Rainey to get his shots every year. This
   is the only reason Rainey would ever have to go to
   the veterinarian.

   _____ **d.** Dr. Cane is a veterinarian in Melissa's neighborhood.
   Melissa said she brought Rainey to Dr. Cane last
   year.

3. _____ **a.** The Pacific Ocean is the largest body of water on
   Earth. It is also the deepest.

   _____ **b.** The Pacific Ocean was given its name because *pacific*
   means "peaceful." The Pacific Ocean is always calm
   and peaceful.

   _____ **c.** The Pacific Ocean has thousands of islands in it. The
   Hawaiian Islands are in the Pacific Ocean.

   _____ **d.** Sea mammals, such as dolphins, seals, and whales,
   live in the Pacific Ocean.

★ ○ The school band concert is being held next Friday
evening. Rehearsals will be every day this week.

○ Four musicians in the band play trumpets.

○ The band put up posters about the concert at the
shopping mall. Many shoppers will come to the concert.

○ Justin's family bought ten tickets for the concert.

Name _____ Date _____

Similes, Metaphors, and Personification

Guided Practice

_____ **1.** The children were as playful as kittens.

_____

_____ **2.** The fog crouched low over the town.

_____

_____ **3.** The stars were diamonds in the sky.

_____

_____ **4.** The moon was an orange balloon.

_____

_____ **5.** The leaves danced in the wind.

_____

_____ **6.** The old bread tasted like sandpaper.

_____

7. like a leaf falling

_____

_____

8. mind was a wheel

_____

_____

9. fear grabbed

_____

_____

Name _____ Date _____

Similes, Metaphors, and Personification

● Read each sentence and underline the figure of speech. On the line before the sentence, write **S** if the figure of speech is a simile. Write **M** if it is a metaphor. Write **P** if it is personification. Then circle the letter of the sentence that gives the meaning of the figure of speech. For the starred item, mark the space for the answer.

_____ 1. When the telephone rang, Cindy shot out of her chair like a cannon, only to hear, "Wrong number."
   a. Cindy injured someone.
   b. Cindy moved very fast.
   c. Cindy was very disappointed.

_____ 2. Sunrise this morning was an explosion of oranges that filled our house with cheer and color.
   a. The sun made a lot of noise.
   b. Even the sun was happy today.
   c. Sunrise was a burst of bright color.

_____ 3. Curiosity gnawed at Luis until he had to open the package that was lying on the table.
   a. Luis's cat, Curiosity, licked his fingers.
   b. Luis was so curious he couldn't get his mind off the package.
   c. A cat nibbled at the package.

_____ 4. The problems were like ants at a picnic, and no one could get rid of them.
   a. The problems were little, but many and annoying.
   b. The problems were like spoiled sandwiches.
   c. We brought our problems out in the open.

_____ 5. The wet road became a sheet of ice when the temperature dropped suddenly.
   a. The road was icy.
   b. A sheet blew into the road.
   c. The temperature on the road made it wet.

_____ 6. The old car choked and sputtered down the street until it died.
   a. Someone choked on the car's fumes.
   b. The car ran over something that died.
   c. The car made a lot of noise until it stopped completely.

_____ 7. Artie's mind is a sponge soaking up any trivial detail that comes along.
   a. Artie's mind wanders a lot.
   b. Artie just got his head wet.
   c. Artie knows lots of little facts.

★ Amanda was a butterfly, flitting from one group to another at the party.
   ○ Amanda dressed up like a butterfly.
   ○ Amanda limped around the room.
   ○ Amanda moved rapidly from group to group at the party.
   ○ A butterfly flew into the room.

Name _____ Date _____

Arctic Fire

● Read each sentence. Find the meaning that fits the underlined word. Write the word next to its meaning.

1. The mountain was <u>immense</u>, so Carl knew it would take days to climb to the summit.

2. The <u>swirl</u> of water in the pool drew leaves into its center.

3. We watched the stray dog hungrily <u>devour</u> our picnic.

4. Spiders weave webs in which insects — their favorite <u>prey</u> — are trapped.

5. Marta turned down the lantern's <u>wick</u>, plunging the room into darkness.

6. Warren worked <u>painstakingly</u> to develop a new program for his computer.

7. The prospector <u>lashed</u> his equipment to the mule's back and headed downstream.

_____ To eat up greedily.

_____ Thoroughly; carefully.

_____ A cord or twisted thread that draws up oil or melted wax to keep a flame burning.

_____ A rotation or spinning as in a whirlpool.

_____ Held securely in place with rope, cord, etc.

_____ Of great size, extent, degree, etc.

_____ Animals hunted or seized by another for food.

● Write a paragraph using three of the underlined words.

_____

_____

_____

_____

_____

Name _____ Date _____

Arctic Fire

● Think about the story "Arctic Fire." Decide whether each statement below is true or false, and circle that answer. Then write a reason for your answer.

1. Kayak and Matthew could reach the shore near Frobisher by crossing the broken ice fields in the bay.

   True   False

   _____

   _____

2. The presence of the seal saved the boys from danger.

   True   False

   _____

   _____

3. Meeting the bear and the seal was lucky for the boys.

   True   False

   _____

   _____

4. Putting their parkas on backwards didn't help the boys keep warm.   True   False

   _____

   _____

5. Both Matthew and Kayak were responsible for being rescued.

   True   False

   _____

   _____

Name _____   Date _____

Maps

● Study the physical map of Wyoming.
Use the information from the map to
answer the questions.

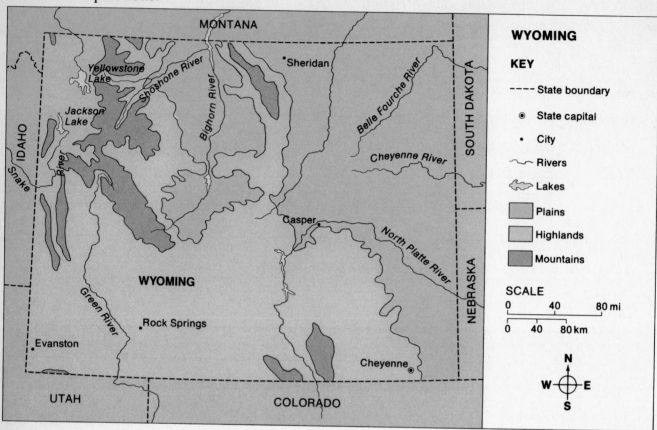

1. How are mountains shown? _____

2. How are plains shown? _____

3. Which cities are located in the plains? _____

4. Which river flows through Casper? _____

5. Which cities are located in the highlands? _____

6. Where are most of Wyoming's mountains located? _____

7. In which part of the state are the plains located? _____

8. Which kinds of land are found around Casper? _____

9. Which river flows from Lake Jackson? _____

10. Which kind of land is found around Sheridan? _____

Name _____ Date _____

Maps

- Study the product map of Wyoming.
Use the information from the map to
answer the questions.

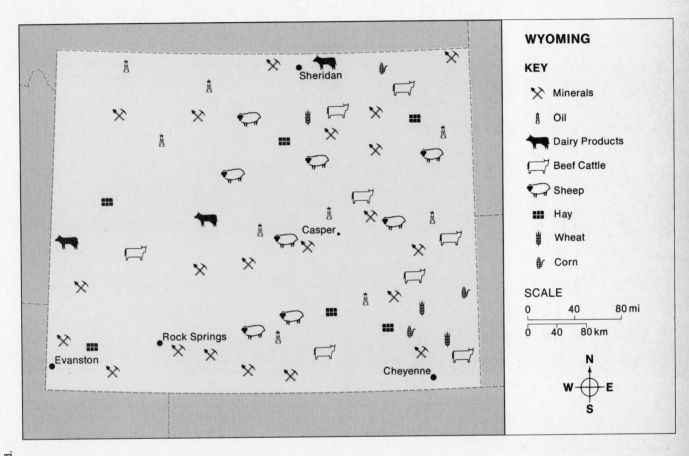

1. How is oil shown? _____

2. How are minerals shown? _____

3. How is corn shown? _____

4. Where is most of Wyoming's wheat and corn produced? _____

5. Which kinds of livestock are found near Casper? _____

6. Which crops are grown near Cheyenne? _____

7. Near which city can dairy products be found? _____

8. Near which city is oil produced? _____

Name _____ Date _____

Denotation and Connotation

Guided Practice

1. I was <u>given</u> first prize.

   I was <u>awarded</u> first prize.

   _____ _____

2. The <u>crowd</u> waited impatiently outside.

   The <u>mob</u> waited impatiently outside.

   _____ _____

3. Someone was <u>staring</u> at me.

   Someone was <u>looking</u> at me.

   _____ _____

4. The fire was <u>burning</u> out of control.

   The fire was <u>blazing</u> out of control.

   _____ _____

5. My (house, home) is always warm and (cozy, comfortable) at Thanksgiving. The (smell, aroma) of turkey and freshly baked bread fills the air. Everyone feels (full, satisfied) after a (mouth watering, good) meal.

Name _____ **Date** _____

Denotation and Connotation

● Read the sentences in each item. The underlined words have dictionary definitions, or denotations, that are related. Put an **X** by the sentence with the word that best answers each question about connotations. For the starred item, mark the space for the answer.

1. Which underlined word has the most favorable connotation?

   ____ The fresh rolls were good.
   ____ The fresh rolls were delicious.
   ____ The fresh rolls were tasty.

2. Which underlined word has the least favorable connotation?
   ____ At the concert, the audience sang along noisily.
   ____ At the concert, the audience sang along loudly.
   ____ At the concert, the audience sang along boisterously.

3. Which underlined word has the least favorable connotation?

   ____ The dark house looked abandoned, but the door was locked.
   ____ The dark house looked empty, but the door was locked.
   ____ The dark house looked unoccupied, but the door was locked.

4. Which underlined word has the least favorable connotation?

   ____ That store sells discounted clothing.
   ____ That store sells inexpensive clothing.
   ____ That store sells cheap clothing.

5. Which underlined word has the most favorable connotation?

   ____ As he recopied his paper, John was meticulous.
   ____ As he recopied his paper, John was neat.
   ____ As he recopied his paper, John was careful.

6. Which underlined word has the least favorable connotation?

   ____ The new student seems very quiet.
   ____ The new student seems very shy.
   ____ The new student seems very aloof.

★ Which underlined word has the least favorable connotation?
   ○ Mr. Lewis likes to repair four-door sedans.
   ○ Mr. Lewis likes to repair jalopies.
   ○ Mr. Lewis likes to repair station wagons.
   ○ Mr. Lewis likes to repair antique cars.

Name _____   Date _____

On Little Cat Feet

● Each word in the box is defined in one of the sentences. Choose the word that completes each definition and write it in the sentence.

buoy	mooring	brusque	reminisce
gaff	dinghy	pungent	fouled

1. A _____ is a small open boat.

2. A small float used as a channel marker is called a _____.

3. A _____ is an iron hook used for landing heavy fish.

4. A place where a boat can be tied is called a _____.

5. To recall and talk about things from the past is to _____.

6. A sharp or acrid taste or smell is _____.

7. To be _____ is to be rudely abrupt in speech or manner.

8. To be _____ is to be tangled up or jammed.

● Use words from the box to complete the sentences.

1. The pirate captain attempted to lower the _____, but its lines were _____ in the railing.

2. Suddenly, the captain's speech became _____ and his manner quite nasty.

3. "I'll use this _____ on every one of you!" he shouted, waving it wildly above his head.

Name _____ Date _____

On Little Cat Feet

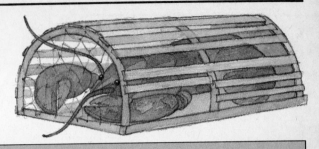

● Think about the story "On Little Cat Feet." Below is a letter that Jo might have written to her brother Roger. Complete the letter by writing one word from the box on each blank line.

fog	shoreline	clock	pulley	wake	nautical	eighty	stories
pots	speedboat	engine	markers	short	lobsters	gauge	keepers

Dear Roger,

What's it like to be a seeing-eye girl? Let me tell you! Aboard the Trudy, which is Uncle Merlin's boat, I give directions by calling it like the _____. It's not _____, but it's quick.

Uncle Merlin has eighty _____. We checked the east forty on our first day out. His _____ are painted white with a blue cross. The first thing you do with a lobster is measure its length with a _____. There are two kinds of _____: shorts and keepers. The shorts are those that don't measure up on the gauge. The others are _____. You should never keep a _____! Yes, I did learn how to pick up a lobster. No, I haven't eaten one.

We checked the west forty on our second day out. Then on the third day we did all

_____. I was feeling proud of myself when I heard a yell, "What o'clock?" I hadn't been paying attention, and he sensed trouble. Heading right for us was a _____! We got out of the way but were hit by the boat's _____. I fell against an iron _____ and got a bloody nose. Uncle Merlin was okay, but he couldn't start our motor. While he was tinkering with the _____, I fell asleep. When I awoke, the Trudy was still drifting. We were enveloped in a thick _____. Uncle Merlin calmed me with _____ of his past. Finally, we both fell asleep. We drifted all night, and by morning the fog had lifted. Was the _____ ever a welcome sight!

Uncle Merlin's quite a man. I'm going to like being his Jo-Eyes.

Love,

Jo

Name _____ Date _____

Topic and Main Idea

● Read the three-part story. Then write a topic for each part of the story and the main idea of the whole story.

1.

Morris had always had a super-duper fantastic time when he went to the big amusement park with his friend Claude and Claude's family — but not this year. The Sky Coaster — that huge, rolling monster — was to blame.

The Sky Coaster seemed to leer down at Morris as he entered the park. It boasted death-defying bends and plunges. Screams and shrieks from its riders could be heard all over the park. Despite these horrors, Morris was expected to ride the Sky Coaster. When you're going into sixth grade, it's one way to prove you're fearless. Morris knew he wasn't fearless; he was scared stiff.

2.

"Let's go," said Claude. "You're not going to chicken out *this* year, are you?"

"Uh, no," said Morris, "but I, uh, think I should stay here with your little sister."

Just then Claude's mother returned to take his sister to the merry-go-round.

There stood Morris, with no more excuses. He could imagine the headline now: NICE BOY DIES OF FRIGHT ON SKY COASTER. Morris saw Claude's disgusted look in the corner of his eye. "I'll go," Morris heard himself saying.

3.

As the ride began, the boys' car crept slowly up a steep hill. Morris thought he was going to faint. At the top, the car hovered for a second, then plunged straight down, dropping with the speed of lightning. "Wow! This is super-duper fantastic," Morris laughed. He shrieked with all the others.

"Isn't this *great*?" Morris yelled to Claude. There was no response. "Isn't this *great*?" he said again. Then he looked over at his friend. There sat Claude — his face a sickly green, his knuckles white.

Topic 1: _____

Topic 2: _____

Topic 3: _____

Main Idea: _____

Name _____ Date _____

Comprehension: Identifying Topic / Main Idea

Unit 21 • CELEBRATIONS

Propaganda Techniques

● Read each item. Decide which propaganda technique is being used. Write the letter of that technique on the line. For the starred item, mark the space for the answer.

A. Bandwagon	D. Repetition
B. Testimonial	E. Emotional Words
C. Transfer	

_____ 1.

Ride Sleekcycle, the cycle of champions.

_____ 4.

Why not switch to BRITE-BRITE? I did, and so did all of my friends.

_____ 2. Robert S. Mith, president of XYZ Corporation, says, "I've traveled all over the world and stayed in many hotels. The service at Baron Hotel is always outstanding."

_____ 3. Tired of the dirt and noise of the city? Come away to Surf Island, where the sea is clearest blue, the sand is sparkling white, and soft breezes rustle the palm trees. Enjoy peace and quiet — away from the maddening crowds.

_____ 5. Food-O-Rama — for all your shopping needs. Food-O-Rama is well-stocked. Food-O-Rama is conveniently located. Food-O-Rama has the best specials. Shop there today!

★ Are you the only one who still isn't in shape? Join BUILTRIGHT HEALTH SPA now. Our professionals will design a workout to meet your needs. Join the millions of Americans who benefit from exercise!

○ Bandwagon ○ Transfer
○ Testimonial ○ Repetition

Name _____ Date _____

Drawing Conclusions

- Read each selection and the statements below it. Write **Y** before each statement that can be concluded from the information given. Write **N** before each statement that is not supported by the information.

Even though Harry and Lance had never been camping before, they decided to go exploring on their own. Now they were lost. Harry thought they should wait for their camp counselor to find them. Lance disagreed. He wanted to find the campsite before it got dark. They began to walk north. At the end of the trail, Harry wanted to turn right. Lance however, wanted to turn left. They were still arguing when their camp counselor found them.

_____ Harry and Lance were inexperienced campers.

_____ Harry could read a map.

_____ Harry and Lance often disagreed.

_____ Harry and Lance should not have gone off on their own.

_____ The camp counselor had been searching for Harry and Lance all day.

Scientists have discovered that dolphins can "talk" to each other by making a whistling sound. For example, dolphins talk when they are sick or in danger. If a dolphin is ill or hurt, other dolphins will carry it to the surface of the water so it can breathe. This prevents it from drowning. The healthy animals will stay with their sick friend until it can take care of itself.

Other scientific tests show that these remarkable animals can learn to solve problems. They can even be taught to say words. Perhaps one day, people will be able to have conversations with these amazing animals.

_____ Dolphins live in the Atlantic Ocean.

_____ Dolphins are intelligent animals.

_____ Dolphins get sick often.

_____ Scientists have learned a great deal about dolphins.

_____ Dolphins need air to live.

_____ Dolphins do not need much water to survive.

Name _____   Date _____

Summarizing

Guided Practice

You probably know that sea water contains large amounts of salt. But did you know that some of this salt from the sea is now being used as table salt? Sea salt can be produced by building special pools near the ocean. These pools are very shallow and open to the sun and air. The pools are filled with salt water. The water evaporates, or dries up, over time, leaving crystals of salt behind.

When the water is completely evaporated, the salt crystals are collected from the dry pools. Then they are taken to a factory. There the crystals are refined and packaged for different uses.

Topic: _____

Main idea: _____

_____

_____

_____

Summary:

_____

_____

_____

_____

_____

_____

_____

_____

Name _____ **Date** _____

Summarizing

● Read each selection. Put an **X** before the better summary. For the starred item, mark the space for the answer.

During Colonial times, roads in America left much to be desired. Made hastily and without the help of mechanical tools, the roads were very uneven. It was not unusual for one side of a traveling stagecoach to be two or three feet higher than the other. Passengers were thrown from side to side and sometimes bounced right out of their seats.

Trees were cleared away, of course, when the roads were made. However, stumps of trees were sometimes left sticking up six or eight inches above the ground. When a wheel struck one of these stumps, the stagecoach often overturned, or the wheel was torn off.

After heavy rains, the mud in the roads might be as much as three or four feet deep. Sometimes it took twenty horses and several hours of work to pull a stagecoach out of the mud. Most of the roads were so narrow that two carriages could not pass each other for long stretches.

_____ Early roads in America were made hastily without the help of mechanical tools. Stagecoaches were often upset.

_____ Colonial roads were very poor. Unevenness, narrowness, jutting tree stumps, and thick mud were among the hazards of early roads.

★ During the 1840's and 1850's, there was a strong push to settle the West. Hardy pioneers often set out on the Oregon Trail, which went for 2,000 miles from Independence, Missouri, into Oregon.

Many hardships beset these pioneers. Boredom was one. Crossing the Oregon Trail took at least four months, sometimes six. Lack of wood to build fires was often a big problem on the treeless plains. Food was scarce and water, when it could be found, was often impure.

○ Despite these hardships, thousands of courageous pioneers succeeded in crossing the Oregon Trail and pushing America's boundaries to the Pacific.

○ Pioneers crossing the Oregon Trail in the 1840's and 1850's faced many hardships. They had to endure boredom, as well as lack of firewood, food, and pure water.

○ Many pioneers traveled west on the Oregon Trail, which stretched for 2,000 miles from Independence, Missouri, into Oregon. The trip could take six months.

○ Pioneers had to cross the Great Plains to get to Oregon. Since the plains were treeless, it was difficult to find firewood.

Name _____   Date _____

From Idea to Air

● Read each paragraph and the words at the right. Circle the letter of the word that correctly completes the sentence with the blank.

My sister Amy studies film and video. At the end of the school year, a contest is held for the best films, and prizes are awarded. The contest is fun, but very __1__.

Last year some students made comedies. Others made adventure films. One student used his drawing skill to make an __2__ film about a frog's adventures in outer space.

Mom suggested that Amy make a film about change. Amy said that the films had to be concrete. One that wasn't about a specific person or thing would be too __3__.

Amy decided to make a film about Grandma, who immigrated to the United States as a girl. I interviewed Grandma. The interview was used as a __4__ to act as the running commentary for the film.

Mom drove us to Grandma's apartment with the equipment. We used a shopping cart as a __5__ to wheel the heavy equipment inside.

Amy filmed for two hours. Afterward, she felt __6__ by the overwhelming amount of film she had shot. But she knew she couldn't use it all.

Amy spent hours selecting the parts of the film that belonged together and cutting the rest. It was a big __7__ job.

I helped her. I timed the sound to the film so the voices and lip movements __8__.

At the contest, Amy won first prize. The judges praised her striking images and the __9__ beauty of her photography.

1. **a.** boring   **b.** silly
   c. humorous   **d.** competitive

2. **a.** intelligent   **b.** animated
   c. important   **d.** ugly

3. **a.** abstract   **b.** exciting
   c. courageous   **d.** engrossing

4. **a.** filler   **b.** background
   c. music   **d.** narration

5. **a.** prop   **b.** dolly
   c. scene   **d.** location

6. **a.** inundated   **b.** sleepy
   c. sad   **d.** angered

7. **a.** dreaming   **b.** editing
   c. laughing   **d.** developing

8. **a.** watched   **b.** taped
   c. synchronized   **d.** erased

9. **a.** peculiar   **b.** dreary
   c. visual   **d.** musical

Name _____ Date _____

From Idea to Air

• Think about the interview with Salem Mekuria. Below are the six stages that are usually required for the production of a television documentary. Briefly, tell what happens at each stage.

1. Research _____
   _____
   _____
   _____

2. Getting ready to film _____
   _____
   _____

3. Filming the show _____
   _____
   _____

4. Preliminary editing _____
   _____
   _____

5. Adding the sound _____
   _____
   _____
   _____

6. Post production _____
   _____
   _____
   _____

Name _____ Date _____

Comprehension: "From Idea to Air"

Assumptions

- Read each group of sentences. Put an **X** before the one sentence in each group that contains an assumption.

1. ____ **a.** Peter Pan is a story character who refuses to grow up. All children feel this way at one time or another.

   ____ **b.** There is a statue of Peter Pan in one of the parks in England.

   ____ **c.** Our school is putting on the play "Peter Pan." My class has been asked to paint the scenery.

   ____ **d.** The play opens in the home of a family called the Darlings. Wendy, John, and Michael are the children.

2. ____ **a.** The class photograph included all thirty students in our room. Each student received two copies.

   ____ **b.** Suzanne's father took the picture. He spent twenty minutes arranging the students before photographing.

   ____ **c.** Suzanne's father is a professional photographer. Suzanne will be a good photographer as an adult.

   ____ **d.** Miss Wyatt signed the back of each photo. She said her hand was stiff after she finished.

3. ____ **a.** All of the buildings in this block are government buildings. This square block is called Government Square.

   ____ **b.** Town Hall has a clock tower. The tower was built in 1856.

   ____ **c.** At noon, the clock strikes twelve. I saw birds in the tower suddenly flap away at the first gong.

   ____ **d.** The post office was built in 1900. It will be time for a new post office soon.

- Underline the sentence that is an assumption in each paragraph.

4. One kind of duck is called a pintail duck. Its tail must look like a pin somehow. A pintail duck has a brown head and a neck with a white line on each side.

5. Those carpenters must be building a garage. There was a garage on this lot earlier. A storm blew it down.

Name _____ Date _____

Time Lines

Guided Practice

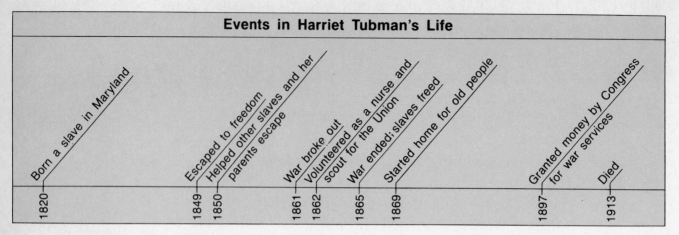

Events in Harriet Tubman's Life

Born a slave in Maryland — 1820
Escaped to freedom — 1849
Helped other slaves and her parents escape — 1850
War broke out — 1861
Volunteered as a nurse and scout for the Union — 1862
War ended; slaves freed — 1865
Started home for old people — 1869
Granted money by Congress for war services — 1897
Died — 1913

_____ 1. Every event in Harriet Tubman's life is shown.

_____ 2. The spacing of the events is important.

---

3. Harriet Tubman began helping other slaves escape in _____.

 a. 1849   **b.** 1850   **c.** 1869

4. When the war ended, Tubman was _____.

 a. 45 years old   **b.** 24 years old   **c.** 65 years old

5. Tubman started a home for old people in _____.

 a. 1869   **b.** 1913   **c.** 1897

6. Tubman helped her parents escape _____ her own escape.

 a. before   **b.** at the same time as   **c.** after

---

7. How many years passed between Tubman's escape and the

 freeing of all slaves? _____

8. What event shows that Tubman still worked for the good of

 her people after the war? _____

Name _____ Date _____

Time Lines

● This time line shows important developments in the history of mail delivery in the United States. Study the time line. Then write an answer for each question below. For the starred item, mark the space for the answer.

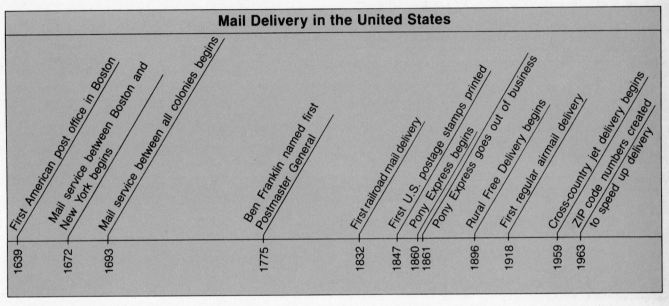

Mail Delivery in the United States

First American post office in Boston — 1639
Mail service between Boston and New York begins — 1672
Mail service between all colonies begins — 1693
Ben Franklin named first Postmaster General — 1775
First railroad mail delivery — 1832
First U.S. postage stamps printed — 1847
Pony Express begins — 1860
Pony Express goes out of business — 1861
Rural Free Delivery begins — 1896
First regular airmail delivery — 1918
Cross-country jet delivery begins — 1959
ZIP code numbers created to speed up delivery — 1963

1. When was the first American post office set up? _____

2. When did mail service between all the American colonies begin? _____

3. What important development happened in 1832? _____

_____

4. How long did the Pony Express deliver mail? _____

5. Which came first — mail delivery by airplane or by train? _____

6. Did Americans use printed postage stamps during the War of 1812? How do you know? _____

_____

7. Were jet planes invented before or after 1960? _____

★ How many years passed between the beginning of the Pony Express and the creation of ZIP code numbers?
○ 106 ○ 131 ○ 324 ○ 103

Name _____   Date _____

Conquering the Colorado

● Choose a word from the box and write it next to its definition. Then write the words, in the same numbered order as the definitions, in the puzzle. If the words are in the right places, by reading down you should find the name of the river that flows through the Grand Canyon.

bivouac	vantage point	pendulum	prow
gunwale	ravenously	portaged	cataract

1. A very large waterfall. _____

2. A temporary camp. _____

3. Greedily eager for food; hungrily. _____

4. A position with a commanding view. _____

5. Carried boats and supplies between waterways. _____

6. The upper edge of the side of a boat. _____

7. A hanging object that can swing back and forth. _____

8. The forward part of a ship's hull. _____

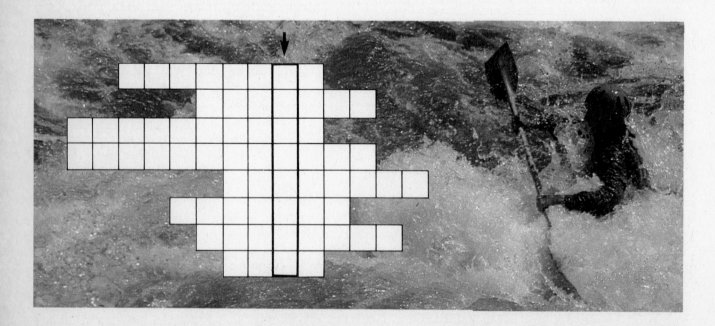

Name _____ Date _____

Conquering the Colorado

- Think about the article "Conquering the Colorado." Below are the names of five things in the article. Tell how each thing was important.

1. *Emma Dean* _____

_____

_____

_____

2. squash garden _____

_____

_____

_____

3. Separation Rapid _____

_____

_____

_____

4. *Maid of the Canyon* _____

_____

_____

_____

5. Grand Wash Cliffs _____

_____

_____

_____

Name _____ Date _____

Similes, Metaphors, and Personification

● Read each sentence and underline the figure of speech. On the line before the sentence, write **S** if the figure of speech is a simile. Write **M** if it is a metaphor. Write **P** if it is personification. Then circle the letter of the sentence that gives the meaning of the figure of speech.

_____ 1. In our town, the summer sun is so hot that the pavement becomes a mammoth frying pan
  a. People fry eggs on the pavement.
  b. In our town, we like breakfast.
  c. The pavement gets very hot.

_____ 2. Night crept softly up, stealing the last bits of daylight.
  a. It was pitch black out.
  b. It turned dark suddenly.
  c. It turned dark slowly.

_____ 3. Carmine's desk drawer was like an old attic because he hated to discard anything he might need some day.
  a. The drawer smelled stale.
  b. The drawer was very full.
  c. Antiques were in the drawer.

_____ 4. Candace disappears like a magician whenever there's work to be done.
  a. Candace leaves quickly when there's work to be done.
  b. Candace is studying to be a magician.
  c. Candace wants a magician to do her work.

_____ 5. Sunny's cheeks are like roses when she comes in from a long walk in the cold winter air.
  a. Sunny grows beautiful flowers.
  b. Sunny has red cheeks.
  c. Sunny gets cold easily.

_____ 6. Our flower-filled garden was a colorful mosaic in the middle of the smooth green lawn.
  a. There were tiles in the grass.
  b. The garden had flowers of many different colors.
  c. The garden needed watering.

_____ 7. Carli felt the cold fingers of fear grab her as the monster appeared on the screen the first time.
  a. Carli's hands were cold.
  b. The movie monster really scared Carli.
  c. Carli likes to act in monster movies.

_____ 8. Mark's spoon was a shovel moving the food from the plate to his mouth.
  a. Mark took lots of small bites.
  b. Mark took enormous bites.
  c. Mark was a construction worker.

Name _____ Date _____

Evaluating Opinions

Guided Practice

A. Title: *The Care of Smaller Pets*
Author: Lawrence Culhane, doctor of veterinary medicine

You should take your hamster to a doctor if its nose is dry
and it refuses to eat. A dry nose and loss of appetite are often
symptoms of serious illness in hamsters.

1. The evidence _____ the opinion.

2. The author is probably _____.

B. Title: *Movies, Movies, Movies*
Author: Marjorie Kane, noted director of award-winning films

Small Wonder was the best motion picture made that year.
The story was warm and believable, and the acting was excellent.
Even the background music was outstanding.

3. a. The author supports her opinion well
and is qualified.

    b. The author supports her opinion
well, but there is nothing to show
that she is qualified.

    c. The author is qualified but does not
support her opinion with evidence.

    d. The author gives no evidence to support
her opinion, and there is nothing to
show that she is qualified.

C. Title: *Sports for Young People*
Author: William K. Wright, author of children's books

The new rules would make youth football a better, safer game
than it is now. Trial games played using these rules resulted in 72
percent fewer injuries than games played by the regular rules.

4. a. The author supports his opinion well
and is qualified.

    b. The author supports his opinion well,
but there is nothing to show that he
is qualified.

    c. The author is qualified but does not
support his opinion with evidence.

    d. The author gives no evidence to support
his opinion, and there is nothing to show
that he is qualified.

Name _____ Date _____

Evaluating Opinions

● Each underlined sentence is a statement of opinion. Write **a** if no evidence is given to support the opinion, **b** if supporting evidence is given, and **c** if supporting evidence is given by a qualified writer. For the starred item, mark the space for the answer.

_____ 1. The Blue Sox are the best team in the league. They have the best-looking players. Even though my sister likes the Tigers, my father and I still prefer the Blue Sox.

_____ 2. The Motor Lynx is the best car on the market today. As a mechanic, I've noticed that the Lynx usually goes many more miles than other cars before needing repairs. The car also gets good mileage — about fifty miles per gallon.

_____ 3. My sister should make a good doctor. She gets good grades in science. She is interested in helping people, and she remains calm in emergencies.

_____ 4. *The Robot's Revenge* is an excellent movie. The plot is exciting, and there are many brilliant special effects. The animation is well done, and the character of the robot is well developed.

_____ 5. The school should build a new gym. I like gymnastics, and I would like to spend more time working on the equipment in a gym.

★ Sue is the best player on the team. In all my years of coaching basketball, I have never seen anyone who could dribble and shoot as well as Sue. She has never missed a practice, and she has scored more points than anyone else.
○ No evidence is given to support the opinion.
○ Evidence is given to support the opinion.
○ Evidence by a qualified person is given to support the opinion.

Name _____ Date _____

Encyclopedia Index

Guided Practice

Light 12: 71-85, 72d
    Astronomy 1:742
    Sun 19:801-802
    See also Stars.
Mars 13:15-20, 18p, 19m
    Astronomy 1:744-745
    Space Travel 19:712-715
Mitchell, Maria 13:92
Mitchell, Mount *See* Mount Mitchell.
Planets 16:100-106
    Distances 16: 105t
    Sizes 16:106c

Rockets 18:708-713,714d
    Jet Propulsion 10:57-59
    Space Travel 19:712-714
Solar System 19:652-658, 659d
    Astronomy 1:744-748
    Planets 16:100-106
Spaceships *See* Space Travel.
        See Rockets.
Space Travel 19:712-717
    Rockets 18:708-712
Starfish 19:800-803, 801p
    Marine Biology 13:45-51

____ **1.** The entry for Maria Mitchell is in an earlier volume of the encyclopedia than the entry for Light.

____ **2.** Subheadings are listed in alphabetical order.

____ **3.** **Space Travel** is listed as a subheading and a main heading.

4. What is the distance between planets Earth and Mercury?

    Volume _____ Page(s) _____

5. How large is our solar system?   Volume _____ Page(s) _____

6. What is Maria Mitchell famous for?   Volume _____ Page(s) _____

7. Is there life on Mars?   Volume _____ Page(s) _____

8. What do starfish look like?   Volume _____ Page(s) _____

9. When were rockets first used?   Volume _____ Page(s) _____

10. What do the orbits of the planets in our solar system look like?

    Volume _____ Page(s) _____

Name _____ Date _____

Encyclopedia Index

- Look at the entries that might be found in the index of an encyclopedia. Write the volume and page number you would use to answer each question below. For the starred item, mark the space for the answer.

Careers C:108	**Diamonds D**:155-163
Adolescent **A**:212	Africa **A**:96
Business **B**:498	Carbon form **C**: 87
Employment **E**:310	Mining **Mid-Myx**:106 *p*
See also individual careers, such as	*See also* **Gems.**
teaching, forestry, medicine.	**Digestion D**: 221 **D**: 222*d*
Detroit, Michigan **D**: 135*p*	Body **B**:256-257
Automobile industry **A**:519	Health **H**:83-84
Economy **D**:138	Insects **I**:312
History **D**:136	**Ernest, Carmen E**:303
See also **Michigan M-Mic**: 592 *m.*	**Etna,** Mount *See* **Mount Etna.**

1. What can young people, adolescents, do to get ready for a career? _____

2. Where is Detroit in relation to other cities in Michigan? _____

3. What does a diamond mine look like? _____

4. Where should you look to find more information about diamonds? _____ _____

5. What kinds of business careers are available? _____

6. What did Carmen Ernest do? _____

7. How do insects digest their food? _____

8. How important is digestion to health? _____

9. What was Detroit like a hundred years ago? _____

★ How important are diamonds to Africa's economy?

  ◯ A:212　　◯ A:96　　◯ D:155-163　　◯ C:87

Name _____ Date _____

Living at the Bottom of the World: My Year in Antarctica

● Complete the story by writing a word from the box on each blank line.

bustling	barren	expel	insulate	bellows
desolate	geyser	log	squid	

All of a sudden I found myself in this _____ land; there seemed to be nothing for miles, only a bitter wind that made me very cold. I began walking, and after a while saw a _____ shooting up hot steam. I went up beside it to try to get warm. That's when I discovered a _____ shack in the distance.

I ran to this deserted-looking shack and found a dying fire inside. I took the _____ and revived the flame.

Then, looking around the room, I found a _____ which told of past adventures at sea. I read about a crew of fishers who were attacked by a huge, leggy _____. Just as I was finishing the tale, a little man came _____ through the door. He became furious at finding me there and would not listen to my explanation.

"Leave at once!" he cried, pushing me out the door. I begged him not to _____ me because it was so cold outside. He only threw me a blanket and said, "This will _____ you."

The next thing I knew I was lying in my bed, grasping blindly for the blanket that had slipped off.

Name _____ Date _____

Living at the Bottom of the World: My Year in Antarctica

- Think about the article "Living at the Bottom of the World." Complete the sentences below.

1. Maria Melgoza Davis and her husband Randy went to

   Antarctica because _____

   _____

2. Weddell seals are unique because _____

   _____

3. The Davises' discovery that seals eat krill was important

   because _____

   _____

4. The seals spend their winters in the water because _____

   _____

5. The seals are able to breathe under the ice because _____

   _____

6. Moving their camp was a problem for the Davises because _____

   _____

7. The Davises went to McMurdo every four weeks so they _____

   _____

   _____

8. Maria Melgoza Davis considered her trip a success because _____

   _____

   _____

Name _____ Date _____

Denotation and Connotation

● Read the sentences in each item. The underlined words have dictionary definitions, or denotations, that are related. Put an **X** by the sentence with the word that best answers each question about connotations.

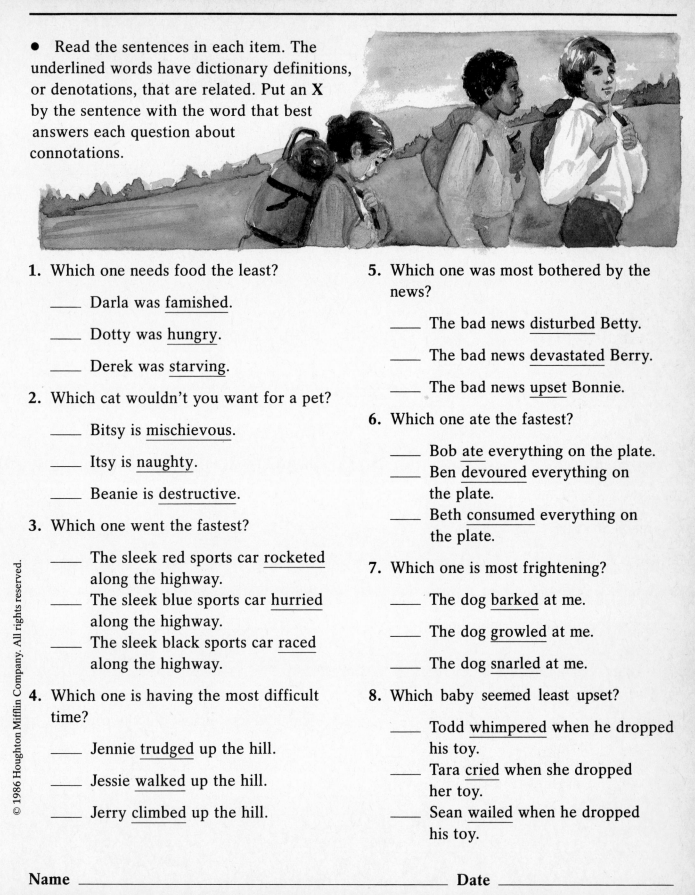

1. Which one needs food the least?

____ Darla was <u>famished</u>.

____ Dotty was <u>hungry</u>.

____ Derek was <u>starving</u>.

2. Which cat wouldn't you want for a pet?

____ Bitsy is <u>mischievous</u>.

____ Itsy is <u>naughty</u>.

____ Beanie is <u>destructive</u>.

3. Which one went the fastest?

____ The sleek red sports car <u>rocketed</u> along the highway.

____ The sleek blue sports car <u>hurried</u> along the highway.

____ The sleek black sports car <u>raced</u> along the highway.

4. Which one is having the most difficult time?

____ Jennie <u>trudged</u> up the hill.

____ Jessie <u>walked</u> up the hill.

____ Jerry <u>climbed</u> up the hill.

5. Which one was most bothered by the news?

____ The bad news <u>disturbed</u> Betty.

____ The bad news <u>devastated</u> Berry.

____ The bad news <u>upset</u> Bonnie.

6. Which one ate the fastest?

____ Bob <u>ate</u> everything on the plate.

____ Ben <u>devoured</u> everything on the plate.

____ Beth <u>consumed</u> everything on the plate.

7. Which one is most frightening?

____ The dog <u>barked</u> at me.

____ The dog <u>growled</u> at me.

____ The dog <u>snarled</u> at me.

8. Which baby seemed least upset?

____ Todd <u>whimpered</u> when he dropped his toy.

____ Tara <u>cried</u> when she dropped her toy.

____ Sean <u>wailed</u> when he dropped his toy.

Name _____   Date _____

Time Lines

● This time line illustrates the order in which some important communication devices were invented. Study the time line to help you write answers to the questions.

Invention of Communication Devices

Braille printing developed by Braille	1829
Photography developed by Talbot	1835
Morse invents magnetic telegraph	1837
Typewriter invented by Soule and Glidden	1868
Telephone invented by Bell	1876
Edison develops phonograph	1877
Loud develops ball-point pen	1888
Marconi invents wireless telegraph	1896
Tape recorder developed by Poulsen	1899
DeForest develops radio tube	1907
Zurrykin creates television tube	1923
Automatic computer developed by Aiken	1939
Color television developed	1953

1. In what year was the radio tube invented? _____

2. Which two inventions were developed one year apart? _____

3. Which was invented first — the typewriter or the ball-point pen? _____

4. How many years passed between the invention of the magnetic and the wireless telegraph? _____

5. Color television was invented how many years after the television tube was created? _____

6. Which inventions were created before the Civil War began in 1865? _____

7. Which inventions were created after World War I ended in 1918? _____

8. Which inventions would you probably have seen in an office in 1880? _____

Name _____ Date _____

Cause-Effect Relationships

Guided Practice

A. The southwest part of the United States was originally settled by the Spanish. Consequently, many buildings in the region still show the Spanish influence. Mountains and rivers have names such as *Sierra Nevada*, which means "snow-capped mountains" in Spanish, and *Rio Grande*, which means "large river." Many cities in the region have Spanish names, such as *San Antonio*, *Santa Fe*, and *Los Angeles*.

1. _____ one cause, several effects   _____ one effect, several causes

2. _____ The Southwest was settled by the Spanish.

   _____ Many buildings show Spanish influence.

   _____ Mountains and rivers have Spanish names.

   _____ Cities have Spanish names.

B. Ginny sat down to do her homework. She had just started when her friend Lisa called. They talked for a while, then Ginny went back to her desk. Suddenly she heard a loud noise from her brother's room. She ran in to see what had happened. Her brother's rock collection had fallen on the floor. Ginny helped him pick up and sort all the rocks. At last she went back to her homework. As she was beginning to work, her mother told her to go to bed because it was late.

3. _____ one cause, several effects   _____ one effect, several causes

4. _____

   _____

   _____

   _____

Name _____ **Date** _____

Cause-Effect Relationships

• Read each paragraph. Then underline the correct answer to each question below. For the starred item, mark the space for the answer.

A. Rob came puffing into the house. He had just raced home with his friend, Rick. Rick wasn't even breathing hard, yet Rob was gasping for breath.

Rob looked at himself in the mirror. "I'm getting thick around the middle," he said to himself. "I've got to do something about this."

Consequently, Rob started a regular exercise routine, including running. He ran for only ten minutes at first, but he soon worked up to fifteen and then twenty.

Rob also started to watch what he ate. He traded his junk food in for fruits and vegetables.

After about a month, Rob looked at himself in the mirror again and liked what he saw. Not only was he trim around the middle, but his skin looked better, too!

1. Which of the following caused Rob to exercise and diet?
   a. seeing that he was getting heavy
   b. losing a race with Rick
   c. building up his running time

2. Which of the following did not happen when Rob started to exercise and diet?
   a. His waist got trimmer.
   b. He breathed hard.
   c. His skin looked better.

B. A tornado hit Smallville without warning. Consequently, no one was ready. The violent windstorm swept the countryside, leaving wreckage everywhere.

Lisle McKinney was taking his cows into the barn when he saw the funnel-shaped cloud approaching. The cows, sensing that something was wrong, took off in every direction. McKinney ran for shelter in a corner of his barn. He was lucky. The tornado's path missed his barn and got only two of his cows.

The Neal family was not so lucky, though they were better prepared. Tess Neal saw the tornado cloud in the distance; therefore, she was able to get her family into the storm cellar before the tornado hit. And hit it did. It swept the Neals' entire house into the sky. Bits of it were found all over.

3. Which of the following caused the wreckage in Smallville?
   a. the cows stampeding
   b. the Neals' house blowing away
   c. the tornado

★ Which of the following was not the result of the tornado?
   ○ the lack of warning
   ○ the Neals' house blowing away
   ○ McKinney's running for shelter
   ○ the cows scattering

Name _____ Date _____

The Dragon Doctor

● Read each sentence. Find the meaning that fits the underlined word. Write the word next to its meaning.

1. The dragon wept <u>piteously</u> when it lost its ability to breathe fire.
2. The horses grazed in the <u>paddock</u> while they waited to be saddled.
3. Sal and Rosa stood at the edge of the <u>sty</u> to watch the piglets.
4. When Lisa broke her leg skiing, the doctor told her she would need <u>surgery</u>.
5. Although an <u>invalid</u> for two years, Max believed that one day he would play ball again.
6. <u>Reptiles</u> are cold-blooded animals; their body temperature changes with the temperature around them.
7. Grandma told exciting stories about her trips to <u>fabulous</u> Nepal.
8. Only a few sheepherders still lived in the tiny mountain <u>hamlet</u>.

_____ The treatment of injury or disease, often by cutting open the body and repairing damage.

_____ Belonging to fables and stories; mythical.

_____ A group of cold-blooded, creeping animals, covered with scales or a shell.

_____ A small rural village.

_____ A fenced field in which horses are kept.

_____ In a way that arouses pity, sorrow, or sympathy.

_____ A fenced-in place in which pigs are kept.

_____ A sick person, often someone who is in poor health for a long time.

● Write a paragraph using three of the underlined words.

_____

_____

_____

_____

_____

Name _____ Date _____

The Dragon Doctor

- Think about the story "The Dragon Doctor." Complete the sentences below.

1. Huang's neighbors respected him

   because _____

   _____

   _____

2. Confucius said he couldn't imagine how to catch a dragon

   because _____

   _____

3. Dr. Ma knew the dragon was ill because _____

   _____

   _____

4. The dragon returned after it was cured because _____

   _____

   _____

5. Huang refused the gift because _____

   _____

   _____

6. The dragon came to live in the village pond because _____

   _____

   _____

7. Dr. Ma felt comfortable in the kingdom of the sky because _____

   _____

   _____

Name _____ Date _____

Propaganda Techniques

● Read each item. Decide which propaganda technique is being used. Write the name of the technique on the line.

| Bandwagon | Testimonial | Transfer |
| Repetition | Emotional Words | |

For the perfect lunch, try Yo-Yo Yogurt. Yo-Yo is light and refreshing — never filling. Yo-Yo is low in calories. Yo-Yo uses all natural ingredients. Have a Yo-Yo and smile! Yo-Yo is right for you-you.

1. _____

Famous jazz trumpet player Luis Locks is shown putting down his trumpet and turning on his radio. He says, "WBJS programs all my favorite jazz. If you like jazz, do as I do — tune into 1030, WBJS."

2. _____

Softo coats are made with a luxurious new miracle fabric. They have the elegant look of suede and the warmth of fur. Pamper yourself this winter. Get a Softo coat.

3. _____

Jack and Jill Jason, famous singers, are pictured in sleek new ski outfits, holding skis. The caption reads: Hit the slopes right in ACTION SKIWEAR. When you look good, you ski well.

4. _____

It's 8 o'clock. Do you know where your friends are? They're watching *The Batty Bat,* the block-buster movie everybody's seeing this summer. Don't get left out. Get in line!

5. _____

BRITE-EYE has the largest selection of eyeglass frames anywhere. BRITE-EYE professionals will take good care of your eyes. BRITE-EYE glasses are guaranteed for 5 years.

6. _____

Name _____ Date _____

Story Elements

- Read the story below, which ends at the top of the next page. Then choose the best answer to each question on the next page. Put an **X** before your answer choice. For the starred item, mark the space for the answer.

"You can't have a pig," Ben Morris told his daughter Kim. "We're produce farmers. We grow vegetables for people, not for pigs. We can't afford a pig, and the answer is no. You can't have a pig."

"But Daddy," Kim interrupted, "a pig would be nice, and I'd do all the work."

"Pigs are a lot of work," said her father. "If we're going to have animals, we should get chickens. At least we could use the eggs."

"But I've saved the money," insisted Kim. "And you're wrong about pigs being a lot of work. They're very clean animals, and intelligent, too. You just don't understand pigs."

"It's my daughter I don't understand," Mr. Morris retorted sharply. "My daughter won't let her hands get dirty in a vegetable bed, but turns around and tries to convince me that she can keep a pig clean."

"I've read a lot about pigs, Daddy. There's a reason they like mud. Pigs don't have sweat glands as people do. They stay in the mud to keep cool. They're not dirty."

Kim's father finally yielded. "Go buy a pig. But it's all yours, and you can keep it only until September. Then it's back to school for you and pork chops for the freezer."

Kim was so excited about getting her pig that she didn't dwell on her father's remark about the freezer. It kept nagging her though, because he had a point. Farming didn't leave much for luxuries, and an animal that didn't result in a product was a luxury.

"I'll call you Noname," Kim said to her new pink piglet. Somewhere she had read that it was best not to name a creature you were raising for food, so she decided on Noname just to be on the safe side. As Noname grew from a piglet into a large sow, Kim became more and more fond of the animal. She had never had such a problem before; it was difficult to become attached to string beans or ears of corn. A pig was different.

"September is a long time off," thought Kim. "And Daddy will change his mind when he sees how nice Noname is." But there was no sign that her father was changing his mind. Kim began to worry.

The last week in August, Kim took Noname to the county fair, where they won a blue ribbon. "A fitting ending," she thought grimly. She bit her lips as she saw her father approaching, and managed to choke back the tears. "I won't let Daddy see me cry," she said. "I'm a big girl now. Right, Noname?"

Name _____ Date _____

Story Elements

"You know, Kim," said Mr. Morris as he congratulated his daughter on the prize, "you've done a fine job with this sow. I think we could keep her. We would not want to turn a prize-winning pig into pork chops. What do you think?"

1. Which of the following best describes the story's setting?

   ＿＿ The story could happen anytime in any rural area.

   ＿＿ The setting is a modern farm in the 21st century.

   ＿＿ The setting is an old-fashioned farm at least a century ago.

2. Which is the initial conflict, or problem, that this story presents?

   ＿＿ Kim's pig is too nice to be taken to slaughter.

   ＿＿ Kim and her father clash over Kim's ambition to do her own thing.

   ＿＿ Kim's father prefers chickens to pigs.

3. What role does Kim's father play in the plot development of the story?

   ＿＿ He is the family's provider.

   ＿＿ He grows vegetables for Kim to feed to her pig.

   ＿＿ Without him, there would be no conflict, or problem, to solve.

4. Which three events help the story build toward a climax?

   ＿＿ Kim gets her pig.

   ＿＿ Kim enters her pig in the fair.

   ＿＿ The pig is kept.

   ＿＿ Kim's pig wins a blue ribbon.

   ＿＿ Kim's father spares the pig.

5. Which event is the story's climax, or turning point?

   ＿＿ Kim's pig wins a blue ribbon at the fair.

   ＿＿ Kim faces her father bravely, even though she feels the pig is doomed.

   ＿＿ Kim's father gives in and lets his daughter buy a pig.

6. How is the story's problem solved and the story brought to a conclusion?

   ＿＿ The pig wins a blue ribbon.

   ＿＿ Kim enters the pig in the fair as one last event to share.

   ＿＿ Kim resolves to be brave, and her father spares the pig.

★ What theme runs through the story?

   ○ Kim struggles against the environment in her pig-raising efforts.

   ○ Kim struggles to show her father that she is a responsible person.

   ○ The forces of good and evil clash.

   ○ Kim struggles to become more like her father.

Name ＿＿＿＿＿＿＿＿＿＿＿＿＿＿＿＿＿＿＿＿＿＿＿ Date ＿＿＿＿＿＿＿＿＿＿＿＿

Summarizing

- Read each selection. Write a summary of two or three sentences for each selection.

1. According to an old saying, necessity is the mother of invention. History seems to prove that this is true. The invention of the alarm clock by Levi Hutchins is one good example. In 1787, Hutchins was an industrious young clock maker in America. Hutchins liked to awake at four each morning, and he became very upset on mornings when he overslept. Finally, Hutchins set his keen mind to solving the problem and invented the alarm clock. Hutchins never received a cent for his invention, nor did he care. He received what he desired — an early awakening each day.

Debt made it necessary for Walter Hunt to invent something. In 1825, Hunt owed $15 and had no means of payment. He sat down with the express purpose of inventing something useful and selling his patent. Three hours later, Hunt had invented the safety pin. He sold his novel idea for $400, paying off his debt with plenty to spare.

_____

_____

_____

2. Many people believe that Thomas Edison was the greatest inventor in history. During his lifetime, Edison received patents on over one thousand inventions. His most famous inventions were the electric light and the phonograph. He also invented a vote-recording machine, a motion-picture "camera," and a telephone transmitter.

Edison's early school experiences did nothing to indicate he would become a world-famous genius. Edison bothered his teacher by asking an endless stream of questions. The teacher thought that Edison's questions were simply "dither," and he told a fellow teacher that Edison was "addled." When Edison's mother heard about this insult, she became enraged and withdrew her son from school. Edison had been in school for only three months, and he never again returned to formal education. His mother, herself a genius as a teacher, taught her lively and curious son by engaging him in games of exploring the real world.

_____

_____

_____

Name _____ Date _____

Word Referents

Guided Practice

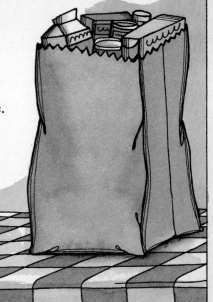

A.

1. "Put the bag on the table," Ernie said, pointing to the table.

   _____

2. Our lawnmower was broken, so we asked Sam and Alice if we could use Sam's and Alice's lawnmower.

   _____

B.

The ¹**girls** waited eagerly for Mr. Clark to speak.

"A class trip sounds great," ²**he** said, "but where will the money come from? There isn't ³**enough** in the class treasury to pay for ⁴**it**."

Lisa and Joanne smiled. Then ⁵**both** began to speak at once.

"We can have a bake sale," Lisa said.

"We can have a car wash," ⁶**her** ⁷**friend** said.

⁸**They** told Mr. Clark that they had already talked to ⁹**their** class about raising money.

"¹⁰**Everyone** will help with ¹¹**this**," Joanne assured ¹²**him**.

1. _____
2. _____
3. _____
4. _____
5. _____
6. _____

7. _____
8. _____
9. _____
10. _____
11. _____
12. _____

Name _____ Date _____

Comprehension: Understanding Word Referents

Word Referents

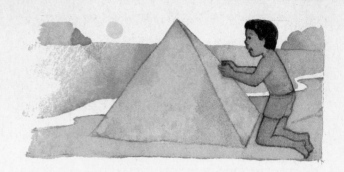

- Read the following story, paying special attention to the numbered words. Then, on the lines below the story, write the word or words to which each numbered word in the story refers. For the starred item, mark the space for the answer.

It had been raining steadily for two weeks. Rick could hardly wait for the first sunny day. He had learned about pyramids in school and was eager to build ¹his own in the sand. Rick looked at the book in front of him. ²It showed many architectural structures that could be built in the sand. In it was a picture of a pyramid.

One morning, his mother woke him early. "It's not raining today, Rick!" she exclaimed. "The sun is out. ³We can go to the beach!"

Rick raced to the window and looked for the sun. Just ⁴then, a cloud covered ⁵it. In and out went the sun, playing hide-and-seek with ⁶him.

Mom and Rick had breakfast, packed ⁷their things, and hopped into the car. As soon as they got to the beach, Rick raced to a spot close to the water. "⁸Here is a good spot," he said.

Rick started to build his pyramid. With wet sand he built a square base. Then he piled damp sand on top of ⁹it and patted ¹⁰that into a rough shape. He carved the sides with a stick and smoothed ¹¹them.

Mom came over and said, "¹²Your pyramid looks great!" Many passers-by stopped to admire ¹³it, too.

Just then Rick felt a drop of rain. Mom said, "You finished just in time, Rick. ★ I think we'd better go now."

Rick took a picture of his pyramid and said, "How lucky that we caught a few hours of sun!"

1. his _____

2. It _____

3. We _____

4. then _____

5. it _____

6. him _____

7. their _____

8. Here _____

9. it _____

10. that _____

11. them _____

12. Your _____

13. it _____

★ I

○ Rick   ○ a passer-by

○ Mom   ○ the pyramid

Name _____   Date _____

To Find a Name

- Each word in the box is defined in one of the sentences. Choose the word that completes each definition and write it in the sentence.

hillock	comforter	mahogany	raveled
locoweed	provisions	convulsive	marauding

1. _____ is a western American plant that makes cattle or sheep sick when they eat it.

2. A _____ is a small hill.

3. Animals or bands of people roving in search of food or treasure are _____.

4. _____ is a reddish-brown wood from a tropical tree used in making furniture.

5. A _____ movement is a violent and uncontrollable contraction of the muscles.

6. A _____ is a bed covering filled with feathers, down, wool, or nylon.

7. _____ are stacks of food and other supplies.

8. Cloth is _____ when its threads have separated and frayed.

- Use words from the box to complete this sentence.

An old, blue _____ with a _____ edge was in the _____ chest packed with _____ set aside for the long, cold winter.

Name _____ Date _____

To Find a Name

● Think about the story "To Find a Name." Write two or three sentences that support each statement below. Use details and events from the story.

1. Even though the boy was tired, Boss woke him soon after she brought him to the sheep wagon.

_____

_____

_____

_____

2. Boss knew that Boy was a "stray."

_____

_____

_____

_____

3. Boss put a sack of potatoes under the covers with Boy.

_____

_____

_____

_____

4. Tex thought Boss and the boy belonged together.

_____

_____

_____

_____

Name _____ Date _____

Vocabulary

● Read each sentence. Then find the meaning for the underlined word. Mark the space for the answer.

1. In spite of what people think, there is no proof that Betsy Ross <u>created</u> the first American flag.
   ○ displayed ○ made ○ built ○ changed

2. For her report on dangerous farm chemicals, Roberta wrote to the Department of Agriculture to <u>obtain</u> information.
   ○ offer ○ save ○ question ○ get

3. The man-of-war bird is known for its <u>swiftness</u>. It can fly 260 miles an hour.
   ○ beauty ○ song ○ sense of direction ○ speed

4. Dave failed his last math test, so he is feeling some <u>anxiety</u> about tomorrow's quiz on fractions.
   ○ worry ○ hope ○ annoyance ○ happiness

5. The three <u>vessels</u> used by Columbus on his voyage to America cost less money than a new car does today.
   ○ drinking glasses ○ sailors ○ ships ○ sails

6. Although chicken soup is not a <u>cure</u> for the common cold, scientists say it does help.
   ○ cause ○ remedy ○ make worse ○ get

7. Some earthworms are tiny and barely <u>visible</u> to the eye.
   ○ ugly ○ dangerous ○ able to be seen ○ able to be touched

8. Mimi barely touched her lips to the <u>rim</u> of the cup before deciding the milk was still too hot to drink.
   ○ side ○ color ○ handle ○ edge

9. John didn't think he could work while he baby-sat, but he <u>accomplished</u> a great deal after the children went to bed.
   ○ completed ○ wrote ○ sang ○ ate

10. After they finished painting the room, Jean and Pedro opened the windows wide to get rid of the unpleasant <u>odor</u>.
    ○ color ○ smell ○ stickiness ○ mess

Name _____ Date _____

Evaluating Opinions

- Each underlined sentence is a statement of opinion. Write **a** if no evidence is given to support the opinion, **b** if supporting evidence is given, and **c** if supporting evidence is given by a qualified writer.

_____ 1. Jane Harmon is a brilliant architect. I have worked as her assistant on several projects, and I am impressed with her inventive designs.

_____ 2. Everyone should learn a foreign language. It's hard to learn to speak and read a new language, but it's well worth the effort.

_____ 3. You should always brush your teeth with a soft-bristled toothbrush. As a dentist, I have observed that soft bristles actually clean teeth better. Hard bristles, on the other hand, may damage your gums.

_____ 4. Stereo records should always be stored in an upright position in a cool place. Records can become warped if they are piled on top of one another or exposed to heat.

_____ 5. Our team is sure to win the next game. We have great team spirit, and we practice every week.

_____ 6. People who disagree should not fight. If they talk things over calmly, they can often reach a compromise that both people can accept. If they get angry, they may make their disagreement worse.

- Now write an opinion of your own. Then write a sentence that provides supporting evidence. Include the source of your evidence or your own qualifications to provide evidence.

_____

_____

_____

_____

_____

Name _____ Date _____

Understanding Characters' Feelings

● Read each passage to determine how the character feels. Remember that you can tell how a character feels by what the author tells you, by what the character says or does, and by how the character says something. Then answer the questions, using the words in the boxes below.

1. Melissa was disappointed. The only thing she had wanted for her birthday was a set of paints, and she didn't get it.

How did Melissa feel? _____

How do you know? _____

_____

_____

2. Josh paced back and forth, waiting for his cue to go on stage. He wiped his sweaty palms on his pants and took a deep breath.

How did Josh feel? _____

How do you know? _____

_____

_____

3. "Don't touch that!" yelled Dick sharply at his little brother, who was reaching for the model spaceship Dick had just finished.

How did Dick feel? _____

How do you know? _____

_____

_____

4. Milton shook hands with his mother's employer, but he didn't look up because he didn't want Ms. Daniels to see him blushing.

How did Milton feel? _____

How do you know? _____

_____

_____

5. Michelle straightened her shoulders, lifted her head high, and smiled broadly as she went to receive her trophy.

How did Michelle feel? _____

How do you know? _____

_____

_____

6. The first time Kenny stayed home alone he was scared stiff. Every little creak made him jump a mile.

How did Kenny feel? _____

How do you know? _____

_____

_____

nervous	proud	angry	shy	disappointed	scared

Name _____ Date _____

Base Words, Prefixes, and Suffixes

Guided Practice

1. Jed belongs to the piano subcommittee of the music club.

   _____

2. The photographer took my picture.

   _____

3. It is impolite to push.

   _____

4. That big old house has a _____ basement.

5. Sandy repeated my words in a parrot _____ way.

6. The captain told the sail _____ to drop the anchor.

7. _____ legal

8. _____ responsible

9. _____ dependent

10. _____ probably

11. climb _____

12. drive _____

13. bat _____

14. carry _____

Name _____ **Date** _____

Comprehension: Using Base Words, Prefixes, and Suffixes to Get Word Meaning

Unit 28 • CELEBRATIONS

Base Words, Prefixes, and Suffixes

● Study these affixes and their meanings.

Prefix	Meaning	Example	Suffix	Meaning	Example
dis-	"not," "opposite of"	*distrust*	-able	"able to" "capable of being"	*reachable*
sub-	"under," "below"	*subbasement*			
sub-	"part of a whole"	*subtotal*	-like	"similar to"	*homelike*
in-, im-	"in," "into," "within"	*indoors, imprison*	-er, -or	"a person or thing that"	*swimmer elevator*
in-, im- il-, ir-	"not," "lack of"	*inactive, imperfect, illegal, irregular*			

● Read each sentence. Study the underlined word. Circle the letter of its correct meaning. For the starred item, mark the space for the answer.

1. Joe's parents want to <u>subdivide</u> the basement so that there is a work area and a play area.
   a. not divide   **b.** divide into parts   **c.** capable of dividing

2. Columbus <u>disproved</u> the theory that the world was flat.
   a. act of proving   **b.** able to prove   **c.** proved the opposite

3. Beth is <u>irresponsible</u> when it comes to being on time.
   a. not responsible   **b.** act of responding   **c.** partly responsible

4. The comedian made everyone laugh with his <u>ducklike</u> walk.
   a. to duck under   **b.** like a duck   **c.** the act of ducking

5. Even though he was deaf, Beethoven became a famous <u>composer</u>.
   a. not composed   **b.** act of composing   **c.** person who composes

6. That big old chair is the most <u>comfortable</u> one in the house.
   a. thing that gives comfort
   b. capable of giving comfort
   c. act of giving comfort

7. It is <u>illogical</u> to expect a young child to sit still for long.
   a. partly logical   **b.** not logical   **c.** person who is logical

★ Fossils, animal <u>imprints</u> in hardened earth, tell us about the past.
   ○ not marked   ○ able to mark
   ○ marks left in something   ○ act of marking

Name _____ Date _____

James Forten Goes to Sea

● Complete the story by writing a word from the box on each blank line.

assailed	magazine	ponder	ramrod	loathsome
muzzle	betray	relenting	gait	belligerent

Ben stood as straight as the _____ he used to pack powder down the _____ of his rifle. He was afraid to _____ his presence to the redcoats who were coming down the road. The British soldiers kept their horses at a steady _____ as they rode past the powder _____ — and Ben hiding behind it.

Ben was on his way to join Ethan Allen and the Green Mountain boys in Vermont. He thought about King George's detestable — indeed, _____ — acts. He also recalled how the king had _____ members of Parliament who sympathized with the complaints of the American colonists. But he knew the king would always be _____, never _____.

"Well, this is no time to _____ over King George," thought Ben. "It is time to act." And Ben continued on his way.

James Forten Goes to Sea

• Think about the biography "James Forten Goes to Sea." Circle the best answer to each question below. Then write a reason for your choice.

1. How did James feel when the *Royal Lewis* surrendered?

    disappointed   panicky   calm

    _____

    _____

2. How did James feel when the captain asked about the marbles?

    worried   angry   embarrassed

    _____

    _____

3. How did Sir John feel about the friendship between James and Willie?

    pleased   worried   unhappy

    _____

    _____

4. How did James feel when Willie suggested he go to England?

    indifferent   pleased   outraged

    _____

    _____

5. How did James feel when he thought of his ancestors who had survived the slave ships that brought them from Africa?

    worried   proud   afraid

    _____

    _____

Name _____   Date _____

Cause-Effect Relationships

● Read this story carefully. Then read the statements below, each of which tells a cause. Write the effect that happened as a result of each cause.

Emery woke up to a rumbling sound in his stomach. He tried to go back to sleep, but the rumblings wouldn't let him.

"I've got to get something to eat," muttered Emery, getting out of bed.

Emery didn't want to wake anyone, so he tiptoed down the stairs without turning on any lights until he got to the kitchen. His sudden appearance there startled the dog, who began to bark.

"Sh-h-h," said Emery, patting the dog on the head. "It's just me."

After the dog quieted down, Emery went to the refrigerator to get something to eat. He reached for a piece of chicken but didn't see the jar of mustard in front of it. The jar went crashing to the floor.

As Emery was cleaning up the mess, his sister appeared in the doorway.

"The dog woke me up," she said sleepily. "What's happening?"

"I was just getting something to eat," said Emery.

"Oh, that chicken looks good," said Sara, reaching for a piece.

"What crashed?" asked Emery's dad, walking into the kitchen.

"Just the mustard jar," said Emery as he dumped the mess in the trash can.

"I'm a little hungry," said Emery's dad, taking a piece of chicken.

Emery washed the mustard off his hands and went to get his chicken, but he was too late. It was all gone!

1. Emery's stomach rumbled. _____

2. The dog started to bark. _____

3. Emery didn't see the mustard jar as he reached for some chicken. _____

_____

4. The mustard jar made a crashing sound. _____

5. Emery's sister and father both ate some chicken. _____

_____

Name _____ Date _____

Learning to Compare and Contrast

- Read each selection, and underline the words that signal comparisons and contrasts. Then circle the letter of the best answer to each question. For the starred item, mark the space for the answer.

Everyone says that Emmie is a miniature version of her grandmother. Both have twinkling brown eyes and dimples the size of dimes. Emmie's hair is the exact shade of brown that her grandmother's is, although Grandmother is beginning to get gray streaks in her hair.

Emmie and her grandmother also have similar interests. Both like the ballet, and both are avid readers. Emmie loves mystery stories, whereas her grandmother prefers historical novels.

Like her grandmother, Emmie is an animal lover. While Grandmother prefers cats and birds, Emmie likes dogs and horses.

1. How is Emmie most like her grandmother in appearance?
   a. Both have gray streaks.
   b. Both have twinkling brown eyes.
   c. Both have black hair.

2. How are Emmie and her grandmother different in their interests?
   a. Emmie likes the ballet; her grandmother doesn't.
   b. Emmie likes to read; her grandmother doesn't.
   c. Emmie likes mysteries; her grandmother likes historical novels.

3. How are Emmie and her grandmother alike with regard to animals?
   a. Emmie likes only dogs.
   b. Both like animals.
   c. Grandmother likes only cats.

Termites and ants have much in common. They are both insects, although they belong to different orders. Ants and termites are both social insects; this means that they live in well-organized colonies. Both termites and ants are noted for working hard and keeping busy. The workers have clearly defined jobs, which they do around the clock without rest.

Unlike an ant colony, a termite society is headed by a king and a queen that stay together for several years. Ant colonies are headed by a queen.

Some winged ants are confused with termites, although their wings are different. Ants have two pairs of different length wings. Termites, on the other hand, have two pairs of wings of equal lengths.

4. How do ants differ from termites?
   a. Ants have two pairs of wings.
   b. Ants are social insects.
   c. Ants' wings are different lengths.

5. How are ants and termites alike?
   a. Both are insects.
   b. Males of both live a long time.
   c. Both belong to the same order.

★ How does a termite colony differ from an ant colony?
   ○ Termites are hard workers.
   ○ Termites have a king and a queen.
   ○ Termites keep busy.
   ○ Termites are social insects.

Name _____ Date _____

Word Referents

● Read the following story, paying special attention to the numbered words. Then, on the lines below the story, write the word or words to which each numbered word in the story refers.

Peanuts and Pepper pressed their noses against the car window. ¹They had never before been to the country.

"The dogs are going to love the countryside," Susan said to ²her parents.

Susan and her parents pulled up to a white farmhouse. As Aunt Carol and Uncle Larry came out to greet ³them, Susan rolled down the window. Peanuts and Pepper jumped out of the car and were off.

The two dogs raced across the meadow, running and jumping. They explored the farm from one end to the other. What a big open ⁴place it was!

When Peanuts and Pepper got to the long red building at the end of the meadow, they peeked in. They did not like the smell, but they ventured further in, in spite of ⁵it. ⁶There they saw some strange black and white animals swishing ⁷their tails. Suddenly,

one of the animals let out a deep, loud "m-o-o-o." Peanuts and Pepper shot out of the barn and back to the car to safety.

"Peanuts and Pepper must be having a great time," Susan said to her aunt and uncle. "We haven't seen them all day."

Later in the afternoon, Dad said, "I'm afraid ⁸we must be going soon."

"I'll go and get the dogs," said Susan.

Susan and Aunt Carol walked around the farm, but ⁹they did not see Peanuts and Pepper anywhere. Meanwhile, Mom and Dad went out to the car to put some things in ¹⁰it. ¹¹There they discovered Peanuts and Pepper — asleep on the back seat!

Dad called Susan and Aunt Carol, "We certainly have funny dogs," ¹²he chuckled. "They were ¹³here in the car while we thought they were enjoying the farm. I guess ¹⁴our dogs are not country dogs after all!"

1. They _____

2. her _____

3. them _____

4. place _____

5. it _____

6. There _____

7. their _____

8. we _____

9. they _____

10. it _____

11. There _____

12. he _____

13. here _____

14. our _____

Name _____ Date _____

Diagrams and Charts

Guided Practice

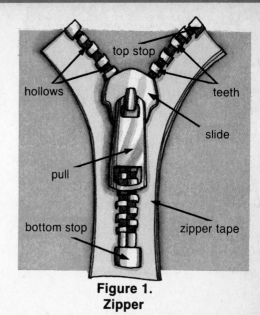

**Figure 1.
Zipper**

The Zipper

The zipper is a type of slide fastener. It is made up of two rows of teeth and hollows which fit together snugly. A slide pulls the edges together so that the teeth are meshed into the hollows. The teeth remain meshed together until the slide is drawn back. Zippers are used on various types of clothing and cases. There are many types of zippers, including one that can be opened from both ends.

_____ 1. With what do you move a zipper up and down? _____

_____ 2. What stops the zipper when it gets to the bottom? _____

_____ 3. What are the small metal pieces on the zipper? _____

_____ 4. What is one type of zipper? _____

Store Employees   The product manager and the advertising manager report to the store manager. The product manager is in charge of the buyers, salespeople, and warehouse workers. The advertising manager is in charge of the artists and the writers.

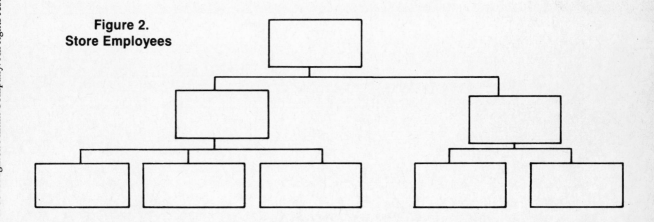

**Figure 2.
Store Employees**

Name _____   **Date** _____

Diagrams and Charts

● Read the paragraph below. Then study the diagram. Use the information to answer the questions. For the starred item, mark the space for the answer.

Tides

The earth's tides are caused by the gravitational pull of the sun and the moon. Although the moon is smaller than the sun, its pull is greater because it is closer to the earth. The closer the moon is to a point on the earth, the greater the pull. This pull forces the water to rise above the waterline, causing a high tide. The farther the moon is from a point, the lesser the pull. This causes a low tide. From the diagram, you can see that a second high tide occurs at the point farthest from the moon. The water at this point is affected by the moon's pull more than the land beneath it. Because the pull on the water is greater, another high tide occurs.

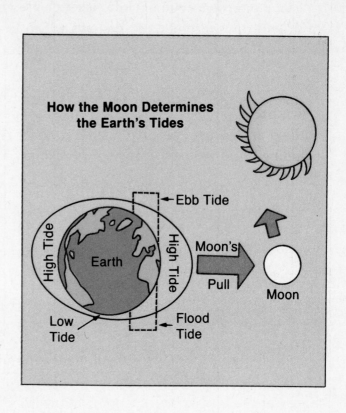

How the Moon Determines the Earth's Tides

Ebb Tide

High Tide

High Tide

Earth

Moon's Pull

Moon

Low Tide

Flood Tide

1. What does the gravitational pull of the moon cause? _____

2. What else affects the earth's tides? _____

3. Why is the moon's pull greater than the sun's? _____

_____

4. What does the moon's pull cause water to do? _____

_____

5. Which tides are shown in the diagram? _____

★ How many high tides occur?

○ four   ○ two   ○ three   ○ one

Name _____   Date _____

Partners in Pictures: The Camera and the Eye

● Read the clues. Then use words from the box to complete the puzzle.

cell	conscious	control	exposure	focus	shutter	aperture
cone	interpret	project	organize	rod	optic	react

ACROSS

4. A cell in the eye that detects light and color.
7. Done with awareness.
9. Having to do with the eye or vision.
10. The small hole in the camera through which light enters.
11. To transfer, or extend onto.
12. The amount of light to which film is subjected.
13. To respond.

DOWN

1. To arrange in an orderly manner.
2. To adjust in order to make vision clearer or more distinct.
3. To explain or make sense of.
5. A cell in the eye that is sensitive to light but not color.
6. To regulate the operation of.
7. The smallest single living unit.
8. Part of a camera that opens and closes to control the amount of light let in.

Name _____   Date _____

Partners in Pictures: The Camera and the Eye

● Think about the article "Partners in Pictures: The Camera and the Eye." Underline the correct word to complete each sentence. Write the word in the puzzle on the line with the same number.

1. In order to see or to take a picture, light rays must be (diffused, focused).
2. Signals are sent from the retina to the (brain, hands).
3. The part of the eye that has color is the (pupil, iris).
4. The shape of the lens in the eye can be changed by (muscles, nerves).
5. Light enters the eye through the (pupil, iris).
6. People whose eyes cannot focus sharply on a faraway object are (nearsighted, cross-eyed).
7. To "see" well, the camera and the eye need the right amount of (speed, light).
8. Light enters a camera through a small hole called an (armature, aperture).
9. When light enters, it falls on the part of the eye called the (retina, pupil).
10. (Nerves, rods) are special cells in the eye that react to light.

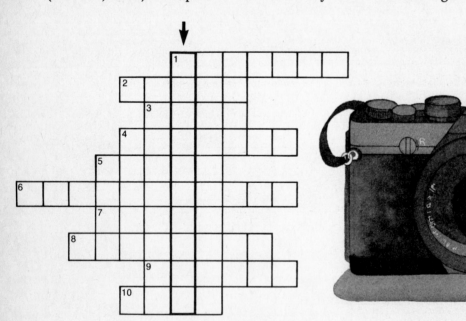

● Now read down at the arrow to find the word that is the opposite of *nearsighted*. _____

Name _____ Date _____

Encyclopedia Index

- Look at the sample encyclopedia index. Use the information in it to answer the questions below. Write your answers on the lines.

Ford, Henry 7:295
   Henry Ford Museum **5**:196*p*
   Mass production of automobiles **1**:620
Foreign population *See* **Immigration.**
Forests and Forestry 7:324-335
   Acid rain **1**:97
   Animals of the forest **1**:295
   Conservation of **4**:412
   Fires and firefighting **7**:109-112
   Petrified forest **20**:521*p*
   See also **Lumber and Lumbering; Trees.**
Formosa *See* **Taiwan.**

Fort Knox, Kentucky **11**:212
   11:213*p*
Forten, James 7:495
Fossils 7:511-517
   Coal formation **4**:312
   Fossil fuels **6**:197
   How imprints were formed **8**:110
   Living fossils **6**:325
   See also **Dinosaurs.**
Galaxy 8:12, **8**:13*d*
   Milky Way **14**:72
   See also **Astronomy.**
Geneva, Lake *See* **Lake Geneva.**

---

1. What animals live in forests?

   _____

2. What does a petrified tree look like?

   _____

3. What is being done to conserve forests?

   _____

4. Where is Formosa?

   _____

5. What did James Forten do?

   _____

6. How did Henry Ford contribute to the automobile industry?

   _____

7. From what other countries have people immigrated to the United States?

   _____

8. What does Fort Knox look like?

   _____

9. How are fossil imprints formed?

   _____

10. Where can more information about fossils be found?

   _____

11. Where are the planets of the galaxy in relation to one another?

   _____

Name _____ Date _____

Quotation Marks
Guided Practice

Two friends were talking about a funny story, "The Bashful Bat."
Julie exclaimed, "Last week I read a story about a bat that
turned red and became invisible whenever it got embarrassed."
"Is red a good color for a bat?" asked Maria.
"No," said Julie, "but the story has lots of facts about bats in
it. I heard the librarian say, 'Many readers will like this story
because it's both fun and informative.' "
"I wonder if I could find 'The Bashful Bat' in the library."
"It's in the March issue of *Nature Facts and Fancy*," Julie said.

_____ **1.** What story are the two friends
talking about?
a. "The Bashful Bat"
b. "A Red Bat"

_____ **2.** Who has read the story "The
Bashful Bat"?
a. Maria
b. Julie

_____ **3.** Which speaker told what the
librarian said?
a. Julie
b. Maria

_____ **4.** Who asked if red was a good color
for a bat?
a. Julie
b. Maria

_____ **5.** Which speaker knew what
magazine the story was in?
a. Julie
b. Maria

_____ **6.** Who hoped to find the story in
the library?
a. Maria
b. Julie

---

7. Francisco said,   My favorite story is   Slithering Snake.

8.   I,   answered Meg,   prefer   The Snoopy Swan.

Name _____   **Date** _____

Comprehension: Understanding Punctuation —
Single and Double Quotation Marks

Unit 31 • CELEBRATIONS

Quotation Marks

- Read the numbered paragraphs, paying careful attention to the single and double quotation marks. Then answer the questions below. Circle the letter of the correct answer. For the starred item, mark the space for the answer.

¹Gene peeked over Carmie's shoulder and saw that she was reading "The Wonderful Wee World" in *Nature Journal*.

²"What are you reading about?" asked Gene.

³"Honey ants," replied Carmie. "They're fascinating!"

⁴"What's so fascinating about honey ants?"

⁵"It says here," answered Carmie, "that 'Honey ants are like living storage tanks. They eat flower juices and honeydew until they grow really fat and round.'"

⁶"Why do they do that?" asked Rhonda.

⁷"When the other ants can't get enough to eat, the honey ants feed them the liquid stored in their own bodies.

⁸"They spend their lives hanging by their feet from the ceilings of their nests. When they get empty, the other ants fill them up again," explained Carmie.

⁹"If you think honey ants are interesting," said Rhonda, "you should read 'Bugs Don't Bug Me' in this month's *Wonders of Nature*. It's funny, but it's loaded with interesting facts."

1. What article is Carmie reading?
   a. "Nature Journal"
   b. "The Wonderful Wee World"
   c. "Bugs Don't Bug Me"

2. Why are double quotation marks used in paragraph 4?
   a. to show that Carmie is speaking
   b. to give the name of an article
   c. to show that Gene is speaking

3. Why are single quotation marks used in paragraph 5?
   a. to give the name of an article within double quotation marks
   b. to refer to another person's words within double quotation marks
   c. to show that Carmie is speaking

★ Who is the speaker in paragraph 7?
   ○ Gene   ○ Carmie
   ○ Rhonda   ○ no one

Name _____   Date _____

The Enchanted Steel Mills

- Each word in the box is defined in one of the sentences. Choose the word that completes each definition and write it in the sentence.

portfolio	mammoth	shrouding
tantalizing	crescendo	silhouette

1. A gradual increase in loudness of music is called a

   _____.

2. A _____ is a drawing consisting of the

   outline of something filled in with a solid color.

3. _____ something means wrapping or

   covering it.

4. A _____ is a case for carrying papers,

   drawings, or photographs.

5. Something that you want and can see but is just out of

   reach is _____.

6. Something _____ is so large it's gigantic.

- Use words from the box to complete the sentences.

1. The _____ grapes hung

   just out of the fox's reach.

2. The clouds _____ the

   mountain made it quite impossible to

   see the top.

3. The noise of the _____

   bulldozer rose to a _____.

Name _____ Date _____

The Enchanted Steel Mills

● Think about the autobiography "The Enchanted Steel Mills." Decide whether each statement below is true or false, and circle that answer. Then write a reason for your answer.

1. In her early days in Cleveland, Margaret Bourke-White photographed steel mills from the inside.   True   False

_____

_____

_____

2. Photographing a working steel mill is very difficult.
True   False

_____

_____

3. Margaret's first photographs inside a steel mill were very successful.   True   False

_____

_____

4. Margaret couldn't find an experienced photographer who could advise her.   True   False

_____

_____

5. Mr. Klaus didn't think one hundred dollars was too much for one of Margaret's photographs.   True   False

_____

_____

Name _____   Date _____

Base Words, Prefixes, and Suffixes

- Study these affixes and their meanings.

Prefix	Meaning	Example	Suffix	Meaning	Example
dis-	"not," "opposite of"	*distrust*	-able	"able to," "capable of being"	*reachable*
sub-	"under," "below"	*subbasement*			
sub-	"part of a whole"	*subtotal*			
in-, im-	"in," "into," "within"	*indoors, impression*	-like	"similar to"	*homelike*
in-, im-	"not," "lack of"	*inactive, imperfect*	-er, -or	"a person or thing that"	*swimmer*
il-, ir-		*illegal, irregular*			*elevator*

- Write the word from the box that goes with each definition.

subgroup	income	comfortable	imprison
statuelike	thresher	impatient	irreplaceable
observer	disapprove	impossible	subzero

1. Not possible   __ __ __ __ __ __ __ __ __ __

2. Part of a whole group   __ __ __ __ __ __ __ __

3. Below zero   __ __ __ __ __ __ __

4. Money coming in   __ __ __ __ __ __

5. Capable of giving comfort   __ __ __ __ __ __ __ __ __ __ __

6. To put in prison   __ __ __ __ __ __ __ __

7. Not patient   __ __ __ __ __ __ __ __ __

8. The opposite of *approve*   __ __ __ __ __ __ __ __ __ __

9. Similar to a statue   __ __ __ __ __ __ __ __ __ __

10. A thing that threshes   __ __ __ __ __ __ __ __

11. Not capable of being replaced   __ __ __ __ __ __ __ __ __ __ __ __ __

12. A person who observes   __ __ __ __ __ __ __ __

- Now write a definition for the boxed word in the puzzle.

_____

Name _____ Date _____

Comprehension: Using Base Words, Prefixes, and Suffixes to Get Word Meaning

Unit 32 • CELEBRATIONS

Bias

Guided Practice

1. _____ *Traffic Troubles Expected at Mall*

   _____ *Charming New Stores to Improve Area*

   _____ *Plans Presented for New Shopping Mall*

2. _____ *Comedy Starring Tasco Opens at Strand*

   _____ *Hilarious Film Tasco's Best*

   _____ *New Tasco Film Flops*

3.

_____ The local baseball team has been left high and dry by Coach Willie Harris, who has deserted Smithfield High School for a National League team. The local team captain reports that he and the other players are very disappointed.

_____ Coach Willie Harris, who has worked wonders with the local baseball team at Smithfield High School, will now have a greater outlet for his talents as he joins a National League team. The Smithfield principal said that the coach's new position was well-deserved.

_____ Coach Willie Harris did not renew his contract with Smithfield High School, where he has coached the local baseball team for the past two years. Coach Harris will be joining a National League team when his present contract expires.

Name _____ Date _____

Bias

Read each paragraph. If the paragraph is biased, underline the bias.

(A) Last night the City Council heard arguments for and against the construction of a new office tower on Myrtle Street. The developers stated that the tower would create new jobs and bring more money into the city. The builders were opposed by members of the Community Protection Association. They said that the tower would bring about overcrowding and decrease the value of all the homes in the area.

(B) Real estate developers last night showed us how much their proposed office tower will benefit this city. The well-designed building will not just beautify the area. It will also boost the city's economy by providing hundreds of jobs and monies needed for much-needed city services. The problems raised by a few overanxious citizens are more than offset by these advantages.

(C) Last night the Community Protection Association vigorously defended the quality of life in our city. They beat back the arguments of developers who plan to deface one of our nicest residential areas with an ugly office tower. Their report showed that the developers are a selfish group of people who have only their own short-range interests in mind.

★ Complete these sentences about the point of view of the writer. Mark the space for the answer.
1. Paragraph A is _____.
   ○ biased for the office tower   ○ biased against the office tower   ○ unbiased
2. Paragraph B is _____.
   ○ biased for the office tower   ○ biased against the office tower   ○ unbiased
3. Paragraph C is _____.
   ○ biased for the office tower   ○ biased against the office tower   ○ unbiased

Name _____ Date _____

Five Under Cover

● Read each sentence. Find the meaning that fits the underlined word. Write the word next to its meaning.

1. By <u>feigning</u> unhappiness, the clown made the crowd roar with laughter.

2. After several hours, the watchmaker said, "I am very tired of examining the inside of this clock <u>minutely</u>."

3. The sailor cleaned, repaired, and painted the boat so that it would be <u>salable</u>.

4. "I can't believe the twins repaired their sled all by themselves," Amy said <u>doubtfully</u>.

5. "This is no laughing matter," Jack said <u>soberly</u>.

6. "Finish your homework before you go skating!" Mother said <u>adamantly</u>.

7. The mouse crept <u>furtively</u> past the sleeping cat.

8. On that fateful day, Sara learned she was <u>destined</u> to be famous.

_____ Pretending; acting.

_____ Stealthily; sneakily.

_____ Uncertainly; unsurely.

_____ Very carefully and thoroughly.

_____ Firmly; in an unyielding way.

_____ Fit to sell.

_____ To be determined beforehand.

_____ Seriously.

● Write a paragraph using three of the underlined words.

_____

_____

_____

_____

_____

Name _____ Date _____

Five Under Cover

- Think about the play "Five Under Cover." Write an answer for each question below.

1. During what period of history does the play take place?

_____

2. Why was it so important that General Washington receive information about the British plans?

_____

_____

_____

3. What made Robert Townsend the perfect spy?

_____

_____

_____

_____

4. How did Anna signal the other Patriots?

_____

_____

_____

_____

5. How did Anna allay the British soldiers' suspicions about her signals?

_____

_____

_____

_____

Name _____ Date _____

Compare and Contrast

● Read each selection and underline the words that signal comparisons or contrasts. Then put an **X** on the line before the best answer to each question below.

Tracy and Trina are identical twins. Both enjoy practical jokes. They love confusing their teachers and friends. Usually they dress alike, from their red-and-white sneakers to the matching hair ribbons in their dark ponytails.

When both girls are looking serious, it's almost impossible to tell them apart. When they smile, however, a clever observer may notice that Trina has a small dimple on her left cheek.

Although they look and sound alike, the girls have very different interests and hobbies. Trina has a pony and rides every day after school. Tracy, on the other hand, doesn't really like animals. She prefers to write songs and practice playing her guitar.

Although modern American football has some similarities to early football, there are many differences. The game has always used some kind of a ball. The object has remained the same: moving the ball down the field and over the opponent's goal line. In modern football, the ball is passed, carried, or kicked toward the goal. But in the early game, the ball was only kicked. The early version used a variety of round objects. The modern game uses only an oblong ball.

Modern football has a time limit. The ball is in play for sixty minutes. The early contests, on the other hand, went on for hours or even days until the players decided it was time to quit.

1. How are Tracy and Trina most alike?
   ____ in their general appearance
   ____ in the way they smile
   ____ in the sports they choose

2. How do Trina and Tracy differ in appearance?
   ____ Trina wears red-and-white sneakers.
   ____ Tracy has a ponytail.
   ____ Trina has a dimple.

3. How does Trina differ most from Tracy?
   ____ Trina has red-and-white sneakers.
   ____ Trina rides a pony.
   ____ Trina enjoys practical jokes.

4. How are both games of football alike?
   ____ Both have the same basic goal.
   ____ Both use the same kind of ball.
   ____ Both last the same length of time.

5. How can the ball be moved in both versions of the game?
   ____ by throwing the ball
   ____ by running with the ball
   ____ by kicking the ball

6. How does the modern football differ from the early football?
   ____ The modern football is round.
   ____ The modern football is kicked.
   ____ The modern football is oblong.

Name _____ Date _____

Evaluating Information

● Read each sentence. Write **F** if the sentence states a fact. Write **O** if it expresses an opinion. If the sentence contains both a fact and an opinion, write **B** and underline the part that expresses an opinion.

_____ 1. The United States has fifty states.

_____ 2. I believe that the most interesting state is Massachusetts.

_____ 3. The first settlement in Massachusetts was at Plymouth.

_____ 4. The settlement was made by people who came from England on the *Mayflower* in 1620.

_____ 5. Those settlers were the bravest people ever.

_____ 6. There are many universities in Massachusetts, and they will help Massachusetts continue to be a center for culture.

● Read the advertisement below. Then answer the questions. For the starred item, mark the space for the answer.

(A) The Maxi-Mower at AAA Lawn Care is what every homeowner needs! **(B)** It has a 2.6-horsepower engine and five attachments. **(C)** This mower will handle any job. **(D)** It is built so well that you'll never use the one-year guarantee. **(E)** Come in today, and you'll agree — the Maxi-Mower is the best one of all!

---

7. Is Sentence A a statement of fact or opinion? _____

8. What is the author's bias? _____

9. How can you tell that Sentence E is an assumption? _____

_____

★ Which sentence from the advertisement states a fact?
○ Sentence A   ○ Sentence C
○ Sentence B   ○ Sentence D

Name _____ Date _____

Bias

● Read each pair of headlines. Then answer the question at the right by writing the letter of one of the headlines in the space.

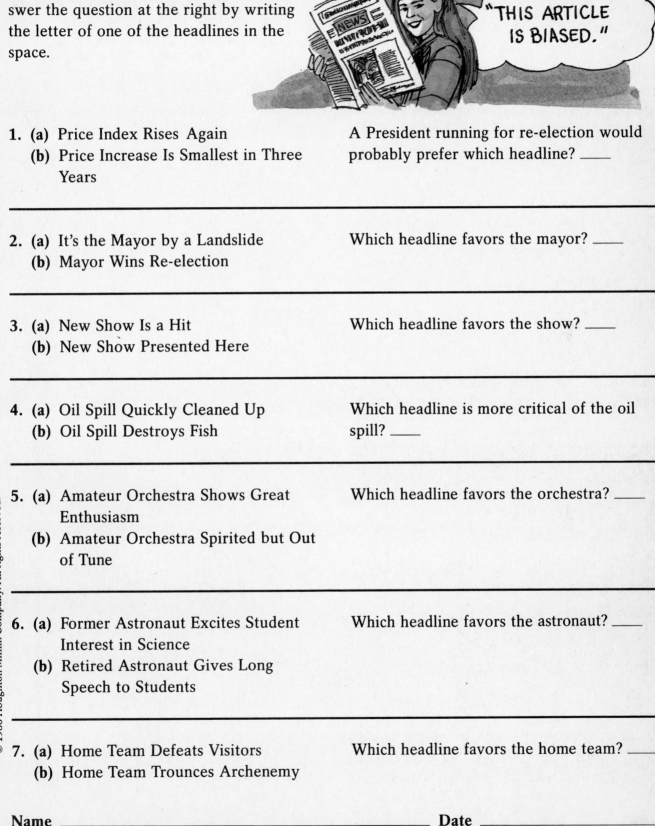

"THIS ARTICLE IS BIASED."

1. (a) Price Index Rises Again
   (b) Price Increase Is Smallest in Three Years

   A President running for re-election would probably prefer which headline? ____

2. (a) It's the Mayor by a Landslide
   (b) Mayor Wins Re-election

   Which headline favors the mayor? ____

3. (a) New Show Is a Hit
   (b) New Show Presented Here

   Which headline favors the show? ____

4. (a) Oil Spill Quickly Cleaned Up
   (b) Oil Spill Destroys Fish

   Which headline is more critical of the oil spill? ____

5. (a) Amateur Orchestra Shows Great Enthusiasm
   (b) Amateur Orchestra Spirited but Out of Tune

   Which headline favors the orchestra? ____

6. (a) Former Astronaut Excites Student Interest in Science
   (b) Retired Astronaut Gives Long Speech to Students

   Which headline favors the astronaut? ____

7. (a) Home Team Defeats Visitors
   (b) Home Team Trounces Archenemy

   Which headline favors the home team? ____

Name _____ Date _____

Encyclopedia

Guided Practice

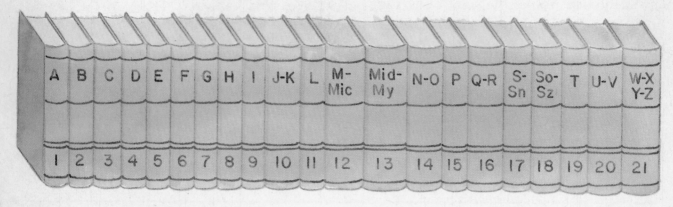

_____ 1. Is the Red Sea red?

_____ 2. What is the difference between a whale and a porpoise?

_____ 3. Who was John Marshall?

_____ 4. Where is San Antonio?

_____ 5. Do sound and light travel at the same rate?

_____ 6. How does radar work?

_____ 7. Who was the first person to reach the North Pole?

_____ 8. Who invented television?

_____ 9. Is Denver the capital of Colorado?

_____ 10. Kitten. *See* CAT.

_____ 11. Fiddle. *See* VIOLIN.

_____ 12. Samuel Clemens. *See* MARK TWAIN.

Name _____ Date _____

Encyclopedia

Guided Practice

Kites

I. How Kites Are Used
    A. Scientific Uses
    B. War Kites
    C. Flying Suggestions

II. How to Make a Kite
    A. Two-Stick Kites
    B. Box Kites
III. Customs and Contests

_____ **13.** Where are kite contests held in the United States?

_____ **14.** How do you make a box kite?

_____ **15.** Who used a kite in an early experiment in electricity?

_____ **16.** How were kites used during World War II?

_____ **17.** What kind of wood should be used in a two-stick kite?

_____ **18.** How do you fly a kite?

_____ **19.** Are there any contests for amateurs?

_____ **20.** Are kites used in science today?

_____ **21.** On what occasion is a dragon kite flown?

_____ **22.** Is it harder to fly a box kite or a two-stick kite?

Name _____ **Date** _____

Encyclopedia

● Read each question, underlining the key word or words you would look up to find the answer in the encyclopedia. Then, on the line before the question, write the number of the volume or volumes that would have the answer.

_____ 1. Where in China are pandas found?

_____ 2. When was Pompeii destroyed by the eruption of the volcano Vesuvius?

_____ 3. What is the Newbery Medal?

_____ 4. Is Mount McKinley in Alaska?

_____ 5. When were postage stamps first used?

_____ 6. What kinds of poetry did Carl Sandburg write?

_____ 7. What are the major products of Texas?

_____ 8. How much nitrogen is in the Earth's atmosphere?

_____ 9. Where are the major cotton-growing areas of the United States?

_____ 10. What marsupials are found in Australia?

_____ 11. How is a house cat different from a tiger?

★ Read the question. Then choose the best answer to the question. Mark the space for the answer.

Suppose you were looking up information on the Liberty Bell. Which guide words would appear on the pages?

○ LENAPE—LENINGRAD   ○ LEOPARD—LIBRARY
○ LIMPET—LINEN   ○ LINGUISTICS—LINOTYPE

Name _____ Date _____

Encyclopedia

● Look at the headings and subheadings that might appear under the main topic **Eye** in an encyclopedia article. Decide which subheading you would look under to answer each question below. Write the number of the heading and the letter of the subheading on the line before the question.

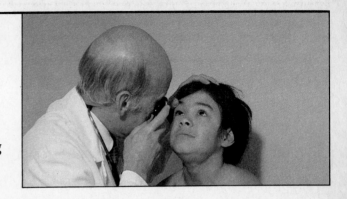

EYE

I. Parts of the Eye
  A. The Eyelids
  B. The Outer Eye
  C. Inside the Eye
II. How the Eye Works
  A. Focusing
  B. The Image on the Retina
  C. Movement

III. Defects of the Eye
  A. Nearsightedness
  B. Farsightedness
  C. Astigmatism
  D. Color Blindness
IV. Eye Care
  A. Vision Tests
  B. Preventing Damage

_____ 1. How often should you have your eyes examined?

_____ 2. How does the eye adjust to distance?

_____ 3. How can a person who wears glasses protect his or her eyes while playing sports?

_____ 4. What fills most of the eyeball?

_____ 5. Does it hurt to have your eyes examined?

_____ 6. What does it mean to be nearsighted?

_____ 7. How much light should you have when you are reading or studying?

_____ 8. What function does the eyelid serve?

_____ 9. What is the colored part of the eye called?

_____ 10. What should you do if you get something in your eye?

_____ 11. How is an image formed on the retina of the eye?

_____ 12. What colors might a person who is colorblind have difficulty seeing?

★ Which of these cross references might provide more information about the eye? Mark the space for the answer.

○ *See also* Tears   ○ *See also* Skeleton
○ *See also* Kites   ○ *See also* Safety

Name _____   Date _____

The Perfect Shot

● Complete these paragraphs by writing a word from the box on each blank line.

telescopic
submarine
periscope
arthritis
blood
slides
elusive
grotesque
convenience
antiseptic

What's so special about scopes? What's special is that they enable us to see things that can't be seen with our eyes alone.

Suppose you are underwater and are traveling in a

_____. Then a _____ is a great

_____. You can look through it in search of

playful but _____ dolphins. Or, if you believe

in the stories of old, you can use it to see whether or not any

_____ monsters are following you.

Astronomers use telescopes. These devices enable them to

determine the position of _____ stars. Biologists

use microscopes to see specimens which have been put on

glass _____.

By using only his or her eyes, a doctor can see to stop

the flow of _____ or to treat a wound with

_____ solution. But to see what's going on

inside your body, doctors use all kinds of scopes — including

stethoscopes and fluoroscopes and ophthalmoscopes. Today,

doctors can even see the changes within a joint caused by

_____ — through an arthroscope.

Wouldn't the ancient Greeks be surprised at what's become of

their word *skopion*, meaning "to view"!

Name _____ Date _____

The Perfect Shot

● Think about the story "The Perfect Shot." Complete the sentences below.

1. The porcupine gnawed the broom

   handle because _____

   _____

   _____

2. Aunt Harriet told Link it was a good idea to carry a compass

   because _____

   _____

   _____

3. Link was willing to stay another week in the woods because _____

   _____

   _____

4. The pied-bill grebe disappeared because _____

   _____

5. Link knew the blue-grey bird was not a crane because _____

   _____

   _____

6. Porcupine quills are difficult to remove because _____

   _____

   _____

7. After the porcupine quills were removed, Link went down to

   the spring because _____

   _____

   _____

Name _____ Date _____

Single and Double Quotation Marks

● Read each paragraph. Notice why the single and double quotation marks are used. Then read each incomplete statement and the three answer choices below it. Choose the answer that best completes the statement. Write the letter of the correct answer.

¹"Hi, Hal," said Vivian. "I didn't expect to see you here in the library."

²"I have to write a paper on the Great Wall of China, and I don't know where to start."

³"I can help you," replied Vivian. "Get a copy of last month's *Great Achievements* and read the article entitled 'The Building of the Great Wall.'

⁴"You can also look in a book called *Wonders of the World*. There's an article in there called 'The Biggest Structure on Earth.' "

⁵"Gee, thanks, Viv," said Hal. "But how do you know all this?"

⁶"Miss Bloom gave us the same assignment she gave your class. I just finished my paper yesterday."

_____ **1.** Paragraph 1 shows that
  a. Hal and Vivian were talking on the telephone.
  b. Hal was talking.
  c. Vivian was talking.

_____ **2.** Paragraph 2 shows that
  a. "the Great Wall of China" is the name of an article.
  b. Hal is speaking.
  c. Vivian is speaking.

_____ **3.** Paragraph 3 shows that
  a. *Great Achievements* is the name of an article.
  b. the exact words Vivian said were "I can help you."
  c. Hal said the words "the building of the Great Wall."

_____ **4.** Paragraph 4 shows that
  a. Hal is speaking.
  b. Vivian is speaking.
  c. *Wonders of the World* is the name of an article.

Name _____ Date _____

Mileage Tables

Guided Practice

Table 3. Air Distance Between Some United States Cities (in miles)

	Indianapolis	St. Louis	Salt Lake City	San Francisco	Seattle	Washington, D.C.
Indianapolis		237	1536	2294	2245	564
St. Louis	237		1368	2126	2109	801
Salt Lake City	1536	1368		759	871	2111
San Francisco	2294	2126	759		827	2869
Seattle	2248	2109	871	827		2748
Washington, D.C.	564	801	2111	2869	2748	

_____ **1.** How many miles is Indianapolis from San Francisco?

_____ **2.** How many miles is St. Louis from Salt Lake City?

_____ **3.** How many miles is Seattle from San Francisco?

_____ **4.** How many miles is Salt Lake City from Indianapolis?

_____ **5.** San Francisco is closer to Seattle than to St. Louis.

_____ **6.** Washington, D.C., and Salt Lake City are farther apart than Indianapolis and St. Louis.

_____ **7.** It would take longer to drive to Washington, D.C., from San Francisco than from Salt Lake City.

_____ **8.** Seattle and Indianapolis are closer together than Indianapolis and Salt Lake City.

_____ **9.** Seattle is placed before Washington, D.C., because it is more important.

Name _____ **Date** _____

Mileage Tables

● Study the mileage table. Then answer
the questions. For the starred item, mark
the space for the answer.

AIR DISTANCE BETWEEN SOME MAJOR EUROPEAN CITIES
(in miles)

	Athens	London	Madrid	Paris	Rome	Vienna
Athens, Greece	—	1486	1472	1303	652	799
London, England	1486	—	783	213	890	765
Madrid, Spain	1472	783	—	650	847	1122
Paris, France	1303	213	650	—	686	641
Rome, Italy	652	890	847	686	—	473
Vienna, Austria	799	765	1122	641	473	—

1. What does this mileage table show? _____

2. How many European cities are shown? _____

3. What is the distance between Athens and Rome? _____

4. What is the distance between Madrid and Paris? _____

5. What is the distance between Rome and Vienna? _____

6. What is the distance between Vienna and London? _____

7. Which city shown is the farthest from London? _____

8. Which city shown is the farthest from Vienna? _____

9. Which city shown is the closest to Madrid? _____

10. Which city shown is the closest to Paris? _____

11. Which city is closest to Athens? _____

★ What is the distance between Rome and Paris?

○ 652   ○ 847   ○ 686   ○ 473

Name _____   Date _____

Lifeboat in Space

● Write a word, one letter at a time, next to its definition.
Then, transfer each letter to its matching square in the puzzle.
You may work back and forth between the puzzle and the definitions in order to find clues for completing both. When the puzzle is completed, you will find a headline for a newspaper story
about trouble in space.

A. A small room in a spaceship or ocean liner.

_____ _____ _____ _____ _____
19   32   14   30   39

B. An element in the air needed for life.

_____ _____ _____ _____ _____ _____
7   24   25   26   11   3

C. People who fly spaceships.

_____ _____ _____ _____ _____ _____ _____ _____ _____ _____
13   43   31   5   23   28   18   2   36   35

D. Referring to the moon.

_____ _____ _____ _____ _____
17   9   16   4   37

E. Necessary; important.

_____ _____ _____ _____ _____
29   15   42   34   10

F. A part of a spaceship used for a special job.

_____ _____ _____ _____ _____ _____
6   38   22   41   33   21

G. Did not have; was missing from.

_____ _____ _____ _____ _____ _____
1   40   12   20   27   8

1G	2C	3B	4D	5C		6F	7B	8G	9D	10E	11B		12G	13C	14A	15E	16D
17D	18C	19A	20G	21F	22F		23C	24B	25B	26B	27G	28C		29E	30A	31C	32A	33F
	TO				34E	35C	36C	37D	38F	39A	40G	41F	42E	43C			

Name _____   Date _____

Lifeboat in Space

● Think about the story "Lifeboat in Space." Decide whether each statement below is true or false, and circle that answer. Then write a reason for your answer.

1. Lowell was able to stop the ship from wobbling by firing small rockets.
   True   False

   _____

   _____

2. If the astronauts tried to ride Aquarius back to Earth, it would burn up.   True   False

   _____

   _____

3. The mission of Aquarius to land on the moon was changed.
   True   False

   _____

   _____

4. The astronauts were able to clean the air in Aquarius.
   True   False

   _____

   _____

5. The astronauts were comfortable in Aquarius.
   True   False

   _____

   _____

Name _____ Date _____

Comprehension: "Lifeboat in Space"

Diagrams and Charts

● Read the paragraph below. Then study the diagram. Use the information to answer the questions.

Scuba Equipment

When scuba divers prepare to go underwater, they require special equipment. They begin with a wet suit. These rubbery suits protect divers from the chilly depths of water. Over their wet suits divers wear flotation vests. When inflated, the vests raise the divers to the surface of the water. Next, the divers need weighted belts, which help them sink down into the water. After putting the swim fins onto their feet, the divers fasten snorkels onto their face masks. When the divers are close to the surface, the snorkels poke out of the water, allowing the divers to breath fresh air. Finally, the divers put on heavy air tanks and strap them to their backs. Just before getting into the water, divers put the demand regulators in their mouths. Since the regulator controls the flow of air from the tank to the diver, it is important that it function properly.

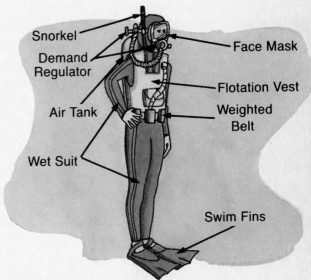

Snorkel · Demand Regulator · Air Tank · Wet Suit · Face Mask · Flotation Vest · Weighted Belt · Swim Fins

1. Which piece of equipment does the diver put on first? _____

2. What is the flotation vest used for? _____

_____

3. To what is the snorkel attached? _____

4. Where does the diver get air from? _____

5. Why is the demand regulator important? _____

_____

6. What connects the demand regulator to the air tank? _____

_____

7. How many pieces of equipment does the diver wear? _____

Name _____   Date _____

Reference and Study: Reading Diagrams and Charts   Unit 36 • CELEBRATIONS   **179**

Diagrams and Charts

● Read the paragraph below. Then study the chart. Use the information to answer the questions.

Language

Language has a family tree, just as you have a family tree. The chart to the right shows two branches of the Indo-European language tree. It shows the relationships between the languages in the tree. From the chart, you can see that Spanish and Portuguese are Romance languages derived from Latin. The chart also shows that Spanish is more closely related to Portuguese than to English. This means that if you speak Spanish, it would be easier to learn Portuguese than to learn English.

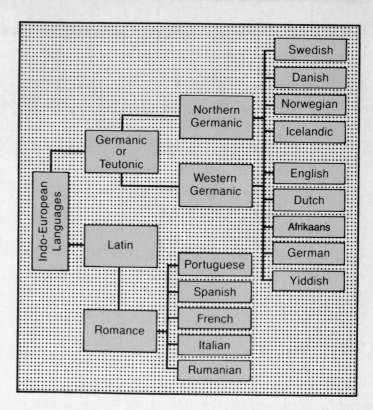

1. How many branches of the Indo-European language tree

   are shown? _____

2. What are the two main branches shown? _____

3. How many branches is Germanic, or Teutonic, broken into? _____

4. In which branch is English found? _____

5. Which language is more closely related to English — Dutch

   or Danish? _____

6. How many Romance languages are shown? _____

7. If you are an English-speaking person, which language would

   be easier for you to learn — Italian or German? _____

8. Which languages are most closely related to Swedish? _____

   _____

Name _____ Date _____

Six Against the Sea

● Read the sentences below. Choose a word from the box to complete each sentence. Write that word in the puzzle.

stern	gamboling	dorsal	paraffin	ichthyologist
dinghy	apathetic	tentacles	specimens	

ACROSS

2. When Mrs. Maxter preserves peaches, she seals the jars with wax or _____.

4. To get to their ship in the harbor, the crew must row out to it in a _____.

6. Mr. Macfin studies fish at the aquarium; he is an _____.

7. Bob dislikes sitting in the front of the boat; he prefers the _____.

8. The octopus uses its eight _____ like arms.

DOWN

1. The doctor took blood samples and sent the _____ to be studied.

3. Lynn didn't care who became the class president; she was _____.

4. The dolphin's _____ fin is located on its back.

5. The children spent the afternoon skipping and _____ about.

Name _____   Date _____

Six Against the Sea

● Think about the story "Six Against the Sea." Complete the sentences below.

1. People often return from an ocean voyage saying there is nothing

   out there because _____

   _____

2. The "flying fish" that awakened Torstein turned out to be an

   important catch because _____

   _____

3. Experts warned Heyerdahl to watch out for the octopus because _____

   _____

   _____

4. Young squid can escape their predators because _____

   _____

   _____

5. Herman fell overboard because _____

   _____

   _____

6. The men knew land was really ahead because _____

   _____

   _____

7. The crew of the Kon-Tiki respected the knowledge primitive

   people had of the Pacific because _____

   _____

   _____

Name _____ Date _____

Comprehension: "Six Against the Sea"

Vocabulary

● Read each sentence. Then find the meaning for the
underlined word. Mark the space for the answer.

1. Early automobiles were much simpler than today's. The first
   autos even <u>lacked</u> such things as heaters and headlights.
   ○ included   ○ added   ○ didn't have   ○ couldn't use

2. Henry Ford began his auto company with only $28,000,
   which would be very little <u>capital</u> for a business today.
   ○ central location   ○ money   ○ planning   ○ product

3. The early Ford factories set up assembly lines. The
   <u>procedure</u> worked so well that a Model T was made in
   only ninety minutes.
   ○ way of doing things   ○ timing   ○ steel   ○ gasoline

4. Early autos had steam engines. The autos were difficult to
   <u>operate</u>, and many accidents occurred.
   ○ build   ○ clean   ○ afford   ○ run

5. Because early cars were so hard to control, riding in them
   was often a <u>chilling</u> experience.
   ○ cold   ○ exciting   ○ dull   ○ scary

6. Most Americans feel that a car is <u>vital</u> to their lives. There is
   now one auto for every two persons in the United States.
   ○ unnecessary   ○ necessary   ○ costly   ○ worthless

7. In the first auto race, in 1894, twenty cars raced 80 miles. A
   steam-powered auto <u>triumphed</u>, clocking the fastest speed:
   17 miles per hour.
   ○ won   ○ lost   ○ broke down   ○ kept up

8. Worldwide <u>commerce</u> in automobiles began early in this century. Today, Japan, the United States, West Germany, and
   France are leaders in the automobile market.
   ○ travel   ○ experiments   ○ trade   ○ battle

9. A flashing yellow traffic light <u>signifies</u> that the driver should
   go carefully.
   ○ remembers   ○ means   ○ decides   ○ happens

Name _____   Date _____

Evaluating Information

- Below are speeches made by two candidates debating each other. Read the speeches. Then answer the questions that follow each speech.

(A) I think my challenger has misstated the record on my support of the tax measure. (B) As you must all know, I have strongly opposed increases in government spending since I came to office. (C) Only during times of greatest need have I suggested raising taxes. (D) For example, when recession hit our state, I supported raising the unemployment tax. (E) This brought in $20 million for those who were thrown out of work. (F) I believe that sort of increase only helps the state.

1. Which two sentences state facts? _____

2. Which two sentences express opinions? _____

3. Which sentence is an assumption? _____

4. What is the speaker's opinion about tax increases? _____

_____

(A) Once again, my opponent seems to have ducked the issue. (B) In fact, she has supported new taxes four times. (C) In 1979, 1981, 1983, and 1985 she voted for tax increases. (D) These increases have cost taxpayers over $60 million. (E) As you can see, she believes in raising taxes any time, not just in times of need.

5. Which three sentences state facts? _____

6. Which sentence expresses an opinion? _____

7. Which sentence is an assumption? _____

8. Which speaker seems to use more facts? _____

Name _____ Date _____

The Day of the Golden Eagle

by Jonathan T. Stratman

"Lee? Lee, it's time to wake up — Lee?" He heard his mother call as she eased up the narrow loft stairs, but he lay still and gave his brain time to catch up. "Lee," she called again from across the narrow loft. "It's time."

his father half-carried him down the narrow stairway, through the kitchen, and out onto the chilly porch under the yellow light. There was the salmon — cut and cleaned, ready to freeze. Laid out alongside was a small cut-throat trout, almost too small to keep, but just the right-sized meal for a king salmon. In the trout's lip was a magnificent, handcrafted bronze lure: the Golden Eagle.

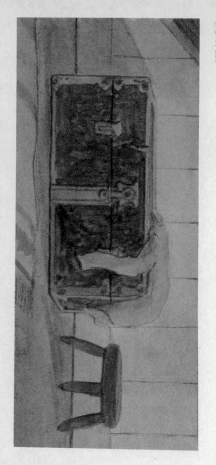

"Okay, Ma — I'm awake." He yawned and stretched, rolled over to the side of the cot, and slowly sat up. Today was the day.

"Lee?" his mother called from the landing, "Happy birthday."

Lee stuffed his feet into his slippers and felt in the darkness for the clothes he had set out specially the night before. While dressing, he stepped to the window and raised it smoothly. The breeze before dawn was fine and soft against his face, and it carried the scent of evergreens into the room. To one side he caught the gurgle of his baby brother Thomas. To the other, the ebb and roll of his Uncle Louie's snores. From downstairs, the murmur of the radio, the tinkle of breakfast dishes, the voices of his mother and father — all familiar sounds, but somehow special today. For a moment he felt old, standing there in the darkness.

"Lee, your eggs are on."

"Coming, Ma." He closed the window and hurried down.

Later, his father shook his hand again. "Happy birthday," he said. "You did just fine, just the way I taught you, just the way I knew you would. Now why don't you go on and hit the sack — I'll clean up this fish."

Lee nodded wearily and started up the stairs. And the day was over. The day of his twelfth birthday, the day of fishing alone, the day of the Golden Eagle. He stopped for a moment in the darkness to gather the sounds: baby Thomas in his crib, Uncle Louie and his parents speaking quietly on the porch, and owl in the evergreens.

Maybe I've been dreaming, he thought just before he fell asleep. Maybe this day never happened.

He awoke, blinking in the flashlight glare with his father's voice rumbling at his elbow. Then he half-walked, and

They talked slightly on the way home. How it had gone — besides the lure — and what a fine day to be twelve, his father said. His mother was silhouetted in the kitchen door as they came up, and she stepped out on the porch under the yellow insect light to have a look at the king salmon. "That's the biggest any of us ever caught," she said, putting her arm across his shoulders. "Louie will probably tell you about some giant fish he caught once, but just you remember, this is about the biggest fish I've ever seen, especially taken on light gear. You did fine."

His father smiled as Lee dropped down the steps into the glow of the kitchen lamp. "How does it feel to be twelve?" he asked and stretched out his hand. Lee shook it firmly.

"It feels fine," he said and looked around the kitchen. "It really feels fine."

They went over it all again as he ate, asking their questions until they knew he had it right.

"Where are you going?" (his mother).

"West — toward Heron Island."

"When do you plan to return?" (his father).

"Before sundown."

His father halted in surprise. Lee was suddenly afraid. All the way home he had been imagining his father's disappointment. Now if he were angry . . .

"That happens," his father said, a familiar, easy voice in the darkness. "Not worth bothering about — we won't make you eleven again for it."

Eleven again. That didn't seem like such a bad idea. If he hadn't had a birthday and turned twelve, he wouldn't have gone out by himself, and he wouldn't have tried out the Golden Eagle, and he wouldn't have fed it to a trout that was likely meant for his father to catch anyway.

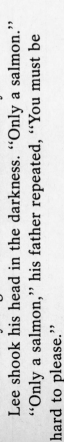

He rounded the breakwater in the faintest afterglow and was guided from afar by the round orange eye of the beacon on their land. His father was there, rocking gently on the beach gravel in time with the lapping waves. In silence, they pulled the skiff up together and stowed the gear in the back of the truck.

"What did you get?" his father asked finally.

Lee shook his head in the darkness. "Only a salmon."

"Only a salmon," his father repeated, "You must be hard to please."

"Dad, I lost it. I lost the lure."

"How many day's supplies are you carrying?" (his mother again).

"Three."

"How . . ." his father paused, "how many minutes can you stay alive swimming in these waters?"

"About twenty minutes. Don't worry, Dad." He thought about the fishing trip as he forked his eggs onto toast and into his mouth. They'd been going out for years, he and his father; now it was time for him to try it alone and show what he'd learned. That was the deal for his twelfth birthday.

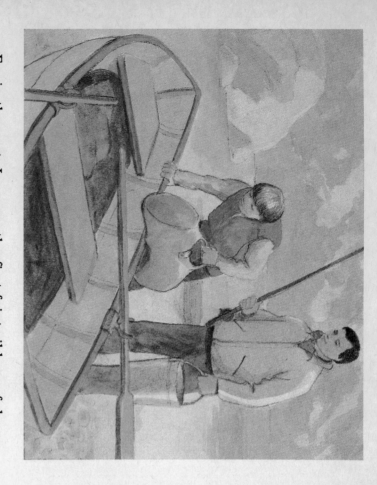

drummed in his head to the rhythm of his oar strokes. He recalled his father hunched over the dining room table with his tools, paints, and magnifying glass. "I'd hate to have to do this again," his father had said. The sun seemed to flow from the sky, and Lee began to row faster.

Far in the east, Lee saw the first faint ribbon of dawn crack like a breakfast egg along the mountain rim.

Within the half hour he and his father were down at the landing. His father stood on the beach gravel, rocking slightly as the waves lapped near his feet, while Lee stowed the gear. The breeze now, and the look of the mountains as they became more and more distinct, was pure August morning. *Today I'm twelve,* he thought again, surprised.

"Cast off," his father called. He stood at the bow line. Lee looked around once more. "Cast off," he called. "I'll be sure to bring home a big one."

"I had that cut-throat," he shouted. He couldn't have broken the line. What was the use of being twelve now?

"I was so sure. . ." He slammed his fist into his open palm till it stung.

Lee reckoned it was about four now; five hours until dark — one hour to fish and four to row home with the wind and tide in his direction. But what for? The whole thing made him want to cry. He sat for a while, almost stunned. Then, mechanically, he set up for salmon.

The hour seemed to go on and on. He had never seen so few fish or had so few bites in his entire life. Finally, when he guessed it was five o'clock and dug deep in his inside pocket for his railroad watch to make sure, he turned the boat. Still trolling, he began to row for home.

As he was about to clear the cove, Lee turned for one last look at Heron Island. "What a birthday," he shouted at the cedar snag, high on a knoll above the water. Out of the corner of his eye he saw his line jerk taut; then he heard the reel begin to whine. Startled, he snatched the pole from the holder and began to play the fish. From time to time he caught sight of a broad pink underbelly. "A king salmon, it looks like a king salmon." It wasn't a cut-throat, but he could see that it was a beautiful fish, and the biggest he had ever hooked into. He knew his gear was too light; even so, he set out to play it for as long as he had to. In forty minutes somehow the fish was his, flopping about in the bottom of the skiff.

But he couldn't take much pleasure in his catch. The loss of the Golden Eagle gnawed at him all the way home. "I lost the lure — I lost the Golden Eagle." The words

"The only big one we need at home is you," said his father. "On time."

Lee took the oars as his father shoved him away. In minutes he was rounding the breakwater. He turned for a last look. His father was still standing there, waving him out of sight.

"A snag," cried Lee, but the line still traveled, so he knew it wasn't caught. He struggled to play it smoothly, all the while searching the deep green water for another glimpse of the silver trout. There was no sign of it. Instead he saw a large, dark shadow near the end of his line. What was happening? It came to him suddenly: a big fish or a seal was after his trout. He came back on the line hard, bracing himself and pulling with his full weight. He had to raise the trout out of the water, out of the reach of that dark shadow. As Lee half stood in the skiff, the line suddenly broke, and he tumbled backward over the seat and into the bottom of the boat. In startled silence he twirled the reel handle, flashing the line aboard. Empty. Swivels, weights, leader, and the Golden Eagle — all gone. Lee struggled up and searched the water for a glimpse of a seal. There was no seal. What had stolen his trout?

The gentle swell outside the breakwater always caught him unexpectedly, though he'd rowed out here hundreds of times with friends. Ahead of him — misty, still gray in the shadow of the mountains — were the islands. There were probably a hundred of them: deserted, wooded with easy beaches, or rocky with the piling surf. He knew many of them by heart. He recalled coming out with his father to pull logs off the beaches to build barns or sell to the mills. He knew the animal trails and berry patches.

Lee settled into a strong smooth pull on the oars, and the skiff cut through the water. Just for an instant he caught sight of his destination — the humped bulge of Heron Island, farthest out of these near islands, capped by a majestic cedar snag. It was said that fifty years ago,

clear, but the reflection of the lowering sun made everything sparkle. He was straining his eyes to follow the lure, when there was a sudden silver flash, and the Eagle was gone. "A fish?" he asked himself, already beginning to reel in.

One fish — the only lousy bite the whole afternoon — but a *silver* fish . . . Could it be? Lee could imagine his father's face if he brought home a cut-throat. It was too much to hope for. The pole dipped; Lee slacked off and then reeled in some more. Again and again, he cautiously played the fish toward the boat. Suddenly it leaped. Lee shouted. It was a trout! Not a big trout but proof that there were trout, and that the lure really worked. There, it flashed again. Lee found himself laughing and whooping and shouting. He was right in the middle of a laugh or a whoop or a shout when he felt a terrible weight on the line, and the pole flexed in a great arc.

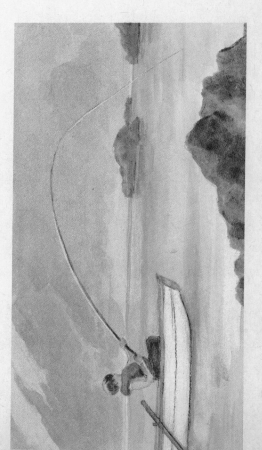

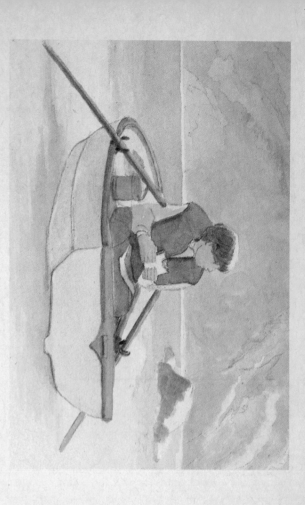

As the tide began to slide back out, he allowed the skiff to ride along. Drifting in the salt marsh, he played the brilliant lure through the grasses and along the cloudy bottom. Now and again he would lean over the oarlocks and catch sight of the Eagle. I'd want to go for that myself if I were a cut-throat, he thought, but still nothing happened.

Lee was feeling a little desperate as he slid back through the cut into the deeper water of the cove. He ate part of another sandwich and drank some juice while he played the Golden Eagle all the way down in the craggy rocks. He could picture the silver trout deep under rock shelves watching that crazy lure go past. Out in the open it was difficult to keep the Eagle in sight. The water was

hundreds of herons had waded the tides and fished off those sands. Under his jacket and sweater, Lee began to be warm. He knew he was keeping the right pace.

Twelve years old, the difference between one day and the next. Yesterday he was forbidden to make an all-day run without his father. Today he was alone on the early swells. The sun pushed through the upper branches on a nearby island, and the water went green around him. As each oar turned up a froth of air, it made a swirl like an expanding bull's eye.

Bobbing easily off Skipjack Cove, Lee ate lunch and went over his tackle. He reckoned it was about ten-thirty — still early — but he'd already done a four-hour row, and he was hungry. He replaced the tackle and started to

close the box when something caught his eye. It was a folded piece of paper, tucked tight against the plastic box that held his lures. As he pulled it out, he saw his father's tight penciled handwriting and felt the weight and the telltale bulge between the folds. "It couldn't be . . ." he said aloud, but it was — the Golden Eagle.

Now, with the Golden Eagle double knotted to a forty-pound test line, Lee trolled into the cove along Heron Island. The sun was almost straight overhead by the time he was ready for serious fishing, and the tide was full and flowing smoothly through the gravel cut. "Come on in, cut-throat," he said aloud. "Time for lunch." He poked about in the stream outlet for the first hours — casting and reeling, casting and reeling — letting the Golden Eagle strut its stuff. But nothing happened.

14

It went back a long way, this thing about Heron Island and the Golden Eagle. Others might fish for salmon or red snapper — even halibut near here. But for years Lee's father had fished for sea-run cut-throat trout off these waters. And for years he had come home with a dry basket. Even so, he was sure they were there.

A small, clear stream flowed into the salt marsh and out through a cut in the gravel bar off Heron Island. Beyond were large, chunked rocks where trout could shelter, deep and lazy. A long time ago Lee had decided: "I'm going to take a cut-throat out of there." But when he told his parents, his father just laughed and shook his head. "We'll both be eating mush," he said. "Still I know they're out there." That was where the Golden Eagle came in.

Through the long cold winter months — when the small craft warnings were flying straight out and even the heartiest seagoing veterans were sleeping late — Lee's father was busy drawing the perfect cut-throat lure. He had made a special trip one Saturday, driving the rickety green truck to the general store for paints and a big package of paper without lines. On each page he drew one big lure, varying the color and design. The poor ones he fed to the fire; the good ones he put up on the wall in the dining room.

Then one night, very late, Lee awakened to a fumbling at his elbow and the blinding spot of the big flashlight playing over a golden explosion of color. His father's voice was close by his ear. "I've finished drawing," he whispered. "This is it — the Golden Eagle. This is the lure that will catch cut-throat."